# American Language Hub



LEVEL 2A
Workbook

with Key + access to Audio

CHRISTOPHER GOUGH

macmillan education

Macmillan Education
4 Crinan Street
London N1 9XW
A division of Macmillan Education Limited

Companies and representatives throughout the world

American Language Hub Level 2A Workbook with Key
ISBN 978-1-380-04711-3
American Language Hub Level 2A Workbook with
Key + access to Audio ISBN 978-1-380-04705-2


Written by Christopher Gough



First published 2020



Original design by emc design ltd
Page make-up by SPi Technologies India Private Ltd
Cover design based on original design by Restless
Cover photograph by Getty Images/Linghe Zhao
Picture research by Emily Taylor

The authors and publishers would like to thank the following for permission to reproduce their photographs:

**Alamy**/Pietro Recchia p30(cr), Alamy/Gordon Shoosmith p20; **Caiaimage** p16; **Getty Images** pp6, 31(b), Getty Images/Mireya Acierto p11, Getty Images/BakiBG p18, Getty Images/Barcroft Media p27, Getty Images/Thomas Barwick pp13, 38, Getty Images/Blend Images p26(tl, tml, tm), Getty Images/Gary Burchell p7(cl), Getty Images/Caiaimage/Robert Daly p31(e), Getty Images/CaoWei p10, Getty Images/Cultura RF p7(bl), Getty Images/Frank van Delft p31(c), Getty Images/George Doyle p36, Getty Images/EyeEm/Rishabh Arora p37, Getty Images/FotoVoyager p33(b), Getty Images/Aleksandar Georgiev p12, Getty Images/Paul Hanson p9, Getty Images/Izabela Habur p34, Getty Images/Hinterhaus Productions p29, Getty Images/iStockphoto pp21(b), 22, Getty Images/Dave and Les Jacobs p39, Getty Images/kali9 p31(a), Getty Images/Cade Martin p31(d), Getty Images/Maskot p14, Getty Images/OJO Images p21(c), Getty Images/Rebecca van Ommen p26(tr), Getty Images/PeopleImages p30(tl), Getty Images/Spencer Platt p30(bmr), Getty Images/Randy Plett p26(tmr), Getty Images/Qatar Airways p30(br), Getty Images/RgStudio p4, Getty Images/SeanShot p15, Getty Images/Abel Mitja Varela p25(b), Getty Images/Dong Wenjie p23, Getty Images/Franziska & Tom Werner p33(tl), Getty Images/Westend61 pp24, 32, 35, Getty Images/Oscar Wong p7(tl); **PhotoAlto**/Thierry Foulon p21(d).



Printed and bound in Mexico
by Compañía Editorial Ultra, S.A. de C.V.

2021 2020
04 03 02 01

# Contents

# 1.1 Relationships

**Breaking the ice**

## GRAMMAR
### Question forms

**A** **Two guests are talking at Katie's party. <u>Underline</u> the correct option in each question.**

**Mike:** Hi, I'm Mike.

**Lucy:** Hello, Mike, I'm Lucy. It's nice to meet you.

**Mike:** You too. [1]*Do you enjoy / Are you enjoying* the party?

**Lucy:** Yes, I'm having a lot of fun. So, [2]*how know you / how do you know* Katie?

**Mike:** We were in college together.

**Lucy:** Really? [3]*Did you study / Did study you* art history as well?

**Mike:** Yes, but now I work in a bank. Katie was the real artist.

**Lucy:** She's very talented – this apartment is beautiful!

**Mike:** Yes, it is. [4]*Are you / Have you been* here before?

**Lucy:** No, I haven't. She invited me for dinner last month, but I was in New York. [5]*Were you / Was you* here that evening?

**Mike:** Yes, I was and I had a really nice time.

**B** **Complete questions (1–6) with the correct auxiliary verb. Then match with answers (a–f).**

1 What ____ you do?
2 What ____ you studying right now?
3 How ____ you know him?
4 ____ you go to college when you were younger?
5 Where ____ you born?
6 ____ you ever been to Asia?

a We met in college.
b In Canada. I moved to the US when I was seven.
c I'm a lawyer.
d No, but I'd love to visit Thailand.
e Yes, I went to Harvard.
f Economics. It's a little boring to tell the truth.

## VOCABULARY
### People

**A** **Complete each definition below with the correct word in the box.**

children colleagues friends grandparents parents relatives strangers students teachers

1 A family is frequently two parents and their ____________.
2 Your ____________ are your mother and father.
3 Your ____________ are other people in your family, like aunts and uncles.
4 Your ____________ are your parents' parents.
5 ____________ are people outside your family who you like and want to spend time with.
6 ____________ are people you work or study with.
7 ____________ are people who you do not know at all.
8 ____________ help ____________ to learn a subject at school or in college.

**B** **Choose the correct words to complete the email.**

TO : Marie
FROM : Amy
SUBJECT : Hey!

Marie!

How's it going? I'm so busy at work because some of my [1]**colleagues / relatives** at the office are sick. At least I have a fun weekend planned! On Saturday, I'm going to a party with my [2]**students / friends** I'll know most people, but some people will be [3]**strangers / colleagues**. On Sunday, I'm having lunch with some [4]**relatives / parents**, including my cousins and aunt. Most of the family will be there, but unfortunately my [5]**grandparents / strangers** can't come because they live too far away.

How about you? What are you doing on the weekend?

Amy

## PRONUNCIATION
### The alphabet

1.1 **Say the pairs of letters below aloud and decide if the vowel sound is the same (S) or different (D). Listen and check.**

| | | | | |
|---|---|---|---|---|
| 1 | b v | *S / D* | 5 e g | *S / D* |
| 2 | d y | *S / D* | 6 i y | *S / D* |
| 3 | l m | *S / D* | 7 q v | *S / D* |
| 4 | c k | *S / D* | 8 h j | *S / D* |

# VOCABULARY
## Types of people

**A** Read each description below and write the type of person in the space.

1 I'm very sociable. I love communicating and I like knowing that I've helped somebody who has a problem.

p ____________ p ____________

2 

I love cooking and I eat out whenever I can. To be honest, I just love tasting things I've never tried.

f ____________

3 I have four kids and, believe me, it's very tiring. Their dad helps but it's me who takes them to school and cooks their dinner.

m ____________ o ____________ f ____________

4 

I love soccer, football and tennis. If there is a ball and people are trying to win, I'm happy.

s ____________ f ____________

5 My perfect evening is spent on the couch with friends zapping monsters on a screen.

g ____________

6 

I enjoy going to other cities and countries and learning about the culture.

t ____________

7 I regularly write articles about my life online. My friends and strangers love to read them!

b ____________

**B** Read sentences (1–4). Then choose the correct option (a or b) to complete them.

1 I'm an animal ___ but I don't have any pets because my house is too small.

**a** lover **b** owner

2 He's a big coffee ___. Sometimes he has five cups a day!

**a** fan **b** drinker

3 She always thinks good things will happen. She's a ___ person.

**a** positive **b** people

4 They're interested ___ listening to music, so they go to a lot of concerts.

**a** at **b** in

# PRONUNCIATION
## Using a dictionary

1.2 Look at the dictionary extracts (1–3) for three words. Then write the correct word for each extract. Say each word to yourself and then listen to check.

1 ____________ NOUN **/ˈkʌltʃər/** activities involving music, literature and other arts

2 ____________ NOUN **/ˈbjuːti/** the quality of being beautiful or very good to look at

3 ____________ ADVERB **/ˈregyələrlē/** frequently, at uniform intervals of time

# GRAMMAR
## Frequency words and phrases

**A** Match sentences (1–5) with sentences (a–e) that express the same degree of frequency.

1 I **normally** ride my bike to school.
2 I **rarely** eat red meat.
3 I **occasionally** watch action movies.
4 I **usually** travel by bus.
5 I **always** shower before going to bed.

a I text my friends **every day**.
b I go jogging **five days a week**.
c I **hardly ever** play chess anymore.
d **Most of the time**, I watch TV in the evenings.
e I still send postcards **now and then**.

**B** Reorder the words to make sentences.

1 never / at work / Julie / checks / personal emails

________________________.

2 call / I / twice / my friend / a day

________________________.

3 always / can / buy / at the restaurant / You / pizza

________________________.

4 He / ever / to school / hardly / walks

________________________.

5 times / visit / their grandparents / They / a year / three

________________________.

6 Emma / rarely / late / is / for her class

________________________.

## GRAMMAR
### Indefinite pronouns

**A** Choose the correct word in each short conversation. Then cover the answers and try to remember them as you read each question.

1 **A:** Where do you want me to sit?
**B:** You can sit *everywhere / anywhere / somewhere* you like.

2 **A:** Who was your favorite teacher in school?
**B:** Mrs. Dean. She taught me *anything / something / everything* I know.

3 **A:** Did you want to see me?
**B:** Yes, there's *anything / something / everything* I need to ask you about.

4 **A:** Where are you going on the weekend?
**B:** *Nowhere / Everywhere / Anywhere*, I'm staying at home to study.

5 **A:** Can we all have some of that cake?
**B:** Yes, of course. There's enough for *anyone / someone / everyone*.

6 **A:** It's my wife's birthday tomorrow.
**B:** Is it? You should take her *anywhere / somewhere / nowhere* nice for dinner.

7 **A:** Do you want me to keep it a secret?
**B:** Yes, I do. *Nobody / Somebody / Everybody* knows about it yet.

8 **A:** What's the matter? You look really fed up.
**B:** Yes, *anybody's / somebody's / everybody's* just stolen my bike from outside the library.

**B** Find and correct the mistake in each sentence.

1 Does somebody know where Alice is?
2 Everyone are here in the classroom.
3 Would you like everything to drink with your sandwich?
4 Everybody like chocolate, don't they?
5 It's a strange building. I don't know if it's a hotel or anybody's house.
6 Are you sure there's anything I can do to help?

## PRONUNCIATION
### Word stress in multisyllable adjectives

1.3 Say the words below aloud to yourself. Underline the stressed syllable. Then listen and check your answers.

beautiful confident creative curious disappointed hard-working independent responsible sensible sociable

## VOCABULARY
### Personality adjectives, adjective + preposition

**A** Read the clues and complete the crossword with personality adjectives.

Across
3 has a good imagination and enjoys making things
7 keeps things in the correct place and is neat
8 feels uncomfortable meeting new people
9 doesn't need other people's help

Down
1 enjoys other people's company
2 likes work and being busy
4 likes to know and learn about new things
5 avoids doing work
6 has good sense and judgement

**B** Complete the online post below with the correct prepositions.

**Worried_Mom_1970**
I'm worried about my son Josh – he's not enjoying school and his teachers aren't [1]**happy** ____ him. Josh has always been [2]**good** ____ math and science but he isn't [3]**interested** ____ studying anything right now. He's always been [4]**interested** ____ sports but now he never leaves the house. He just watches TV or plays computer games. He doesn't get [5]**involved** ____ any after-school activities either. We try to talk to him and offer encouragement, but he doesn't respond. He must realize that now that he's 15, he's [6]**responsible** ____ his own happiness. What should we do?

## Social Media Personalities

People have always liked labeling other people. Today, journalists at magazines write articles labeling people even when they are online. So, not to be left out, we've put together our Ultimate Top Eight of social media user personality types. Check it out below.

**Fanatics** spend hours on social media sites. They have all the latest apps and continually check them. A quarter of young users spend more than two hours a day updating their social media pages.

**Egoists** want to impress people. They want to have more followers than other users, and they worry about the number of likes they get.

**Watchers** hide and rarely take part in social media exchanges. Almost half of all social media users admit that they observe rather than get involved.

**Novices** are new to social media. They don't yet understand how it all works so they post things now and then, but not very regularly.

**Changelings** have different personalities online. They use false names so other posters don't know their identity. 15% of users say they express opinions more freely when people don't know who they are.

**Informers** like being the first to notice something they can share. They feel good when they can report the latest news and gossip.

**Quizzers** ask questions to start online conversations. They prefer to learn about other people and hardly ever post their own updates.

**Trolls** go online to cause trouble. They enjoy posting negative comments, starting arguments and making other users feel bad.

Most social media users are a mix of these personality types, and they behave differently on different sites. The internet has changed our lives and maybe our personalities too. What type of user are you?

## READING

**A PREDICT** Look at the title, pictures and headings of the article. Then answer the questions.

1 What do you think the article will be about? Choose one option from below.
   - a The most common topics that people look for online.
   - b Some typical ways that people behave when they use social media.
   - c The percentage of people who frequently use social media.

2 Decide if the following statements about the article are probably true (T) or probably false (F).
   - a You can trust all the information because it is based on scientific research. *T / F*
   - b The article aims to entertain readers rather than inform them. *T / F*
   - c You can find a lot of very similar articles online. *T / F*

**B READ FOR MAIN IDEA** Read *Social Media Personalities.* Check your answers to Exercise A.

**C READ FOR DETAIL** Read the article again. Choose a social media type for each person in 1–8.

1 Emma likes asking other users about their interests. ________
2 Julie wants to tell everyone that a famous couple has broken up. ________
3 Max changes his user name every month. ________
4 Leah reads what other people are saying but doesn't say much herself. ________
5 Justin needed help when he posted for the first time last week. ________
6 Holly has just told another user that her post is stupid. ________
7 Gary usually wakes up during the night to check his social media pages. ________
8 Lucy's worried because nobody has responded to her last post. ________

**D REFLECT** Think about the answers to these questions.

1 Do you think social media users really fall into these eight types?
2 What type of social media personality are you?
3 Do you think your personality changes at all when you use social media?

### Glossary

**gossip (n)** information or conversation about people's lives that might not be true
**identity (n)** what makes you who you are and different from other people / proof of who you are
**label (v)** use a word or phrase to describe someone, especially a word or phrase that is not fair or true
**update (v/n)** add recent information / addition of new information

## LISTENING

**A PREDICT** Match the words and phrases to pictures (a–d) above.

1 bow ___ 2 hug ___ 3 kiss on both cheeks ___ 4 shake hands ___

1.4 **B LISTEN FOR DETAIL** Listen to five students talking with their teacher. Complete the notes in the table below with one word in each space.

| Name | Country | Spoken greeting | Physical greeting |
|---|---|---|---|
| *Javier* | 1 ______ | *Hola / Encantado =*<br>2 ______ *to meet you* | *women: kiss on both cheeks*<br>*men: shake hands or* 3 ______ *if good friends* |
| *Amelie* | 4 ______ | *Bonjour = Good* 5 ______<br>*Bonsoir = Good evening* | *women: kiss on both cheeks* 6 ______ *times* |
| *Ahmed* | *Oman* | *Marhaba = Hello* | *men:* 7 ______ *friends touch noses or shake only the* 8 ______ *hand* |
| *Junko* | 9 ______ | *Konnichiwa = Hello/Good day* | *the way a person bows depends on the* 10 ______ *with the other person* |
| *Achara* | *Thailand* | *Sawasdee khrap = Hello for* 11 ______<br>*Sawasdee kha = Hello for* 12 ______ | *bow head forward and press palms of hands together* |

**C REFLECT** Think about your answers to these questions.

1 Do men and women greet each other differently in your country?

2 Are there formal and informal greetings?

**Glossary**

**fascinating (adj)** making you very interested or attracted
**formal (adj)** following the correct or suitable official methods
**tend to (phrase)** to usually do a particular thing

## FUNCTIONAL LANGUAGE

### Greet people and give personal information, make introductions

1.5 Put each conversation (1–3) in the correct order. Then listen to check.

**1**

a **Daniel:** I'm good. Things are going well. How about you … what's new? ___

b **Liz:** Well, I just got back from traveling in Asia. It was amazing. ___

c **Liz:** You too … long time no see! How's it going? ___

d **Daniel:** Hi, Liz. What a nice surprise. It's great to see you. *1*

**2**

a **Claire:** Do you enjoy it? ___

b **Claire:** Hi Gavin, I'm Claire. Nice to meet you. What do you do? ___

c **Gavin:** Let me introduce myself. I'm Gavin. ___

d **Gavin:** Well, it's not my dream job but it pays the rent. ___

e **Gavin:** I'm working in a bookstore for now. ___

**3**

a **Tom:** Sorry, I have to go now. ___

b **Tom:** I have my driving test tomorrow … at 8:30! ___

c **Simon:** Oh OK. Good luck! ___

d **Simon:** Would you like another drink? ___

e **Simon:** Really, why so early? ___

## WRITING

**A** Read Sarah's ad below. What things does she want to know about if you are interested in renting the room?

**Wanted!**

We are looking for a sociable and well-organized person to rent a room in our house.
It's on Staverton Road in the city center.
It costs $300 per month.

If you are interested, email Sarah with the following information: your age, your job, your likes/dislikes, what type of person you are.

**B** Read Carla's reply. Do you think she is the right person for the room?

**To:** Sarah
**From:** Carla
**Subject:** Available room

Hi Sarah,

I'm emailing about your add for the room. I'm very interested with renting it!

I'm nineteen years old and right now I'm a student. I'm interested in watch movies and listening to music. I'm a dog owner, but I don't have any pets.

I'm a people person: I love chating to other people and going out to meet my friends. We usually go to the movie theater or out for anything to eat. I'm very neat and always clean my room – so don't worry about that!

I look forward to hearing from you.

Best wishes,
Carla

**C** Read Carla's reply in Exercise B again and circle six mistakes. Then decide if they are grammar (G), vocabulary (V) or spelling (S) mistakes.

## WRITING PRACTICE

**A** **PREPARE** You are going to write a reply to an ad. Read the ad, then write notes about your work/studies, your likes and dislikes and your personality.

**Wanted!**

Are you a people person and a cat lover? We are looking for someone to share an apartment with three girls and our pet cat!

If you are interested, email Jessica and tell her about yourself. We want to know about your job or studies, what type of person you are and what things you like/dislike.

**B** **WRITE** Write your reply to the ad in Exercise A above.

- Use your notes and ideas from Exercise A.
- Write your email in 50–100 words.

**C** **REVIEW** Remember to check your writing for spelling, grammar and punctuation mistakes.

## GRAMMAR
### Adverbs of degree

**A** **Choose the correct adverb of degree. Then insert the adverb in the correct place.**

1 There are some tall buildings in Dubai – some of them are more than 100 meters high! (*fairly* / *extremely*)

2 The movie was good but I wouldn't watch it again. (*fairly* / *very*)

3 The builders are friendly. They talk to us all the time. (*almost* / *really*)

4 The children are excited about going to the zoo next week. (*so* / *almost*)

5 We won the soccer game, but the other team scored a goal in the last minute. (*completely* / *almost*)

6 Jack has changed since I last saw him. (*fairly* / *completely*)

**B** **In the following conversations, write the bold words in the correct order. Then cover the responses and try to remember them.**

1 **A:** It isn't easy to use the subway in this city.
**B:** I agree, **complicated really it's**, isn't it?
_______________

2 **A:** The test wasn't too difficult, was it?
**B:** No, **really was easy it**.
_______________

3 **A:** The city looks very different.
**B:** Yes, **has the center changed completely**.
_______________

4 **A:** Have you started that book I gave you?
**B:** Yes, **finished chapter almost first I've the**.
_______________

5 **A:** The city feels bigger than it did.
**B:** Yes, **is quickly population the growing**.
_______________

6 **A:** Wow! Your son has really grown!
**B:** Yes, **he's tall a very boy now**.
_______________

## VOCABULARY
### Describing places

**A** **Cross out the noun in each list that the adjective in bold does not usually describe.**

1 **attractive** *building / town / person / music*
2 **ugly** *building / city / person / food*
3 **modern** *buildings / trees / art / furniture*
4 **old-fashioned** *buildings / river / clothes / ideas*
5 **clean** *water / air / clothes / art*
6 **loud** *noise / sky / music / voice*

**B** **Complete the sentences with the correct adjective form of the word in parentheses.**

1 The streets are very _______________ in this part of town. (*dirt*)

2 The park is very _______________. I go there to relax. (*peace*)

3 There are no bus stops near our house. It's very _______________. (*convenience*)

4 This music is boring. Can I put on something more _______________? (*live*)

**C** **Choose an adjective from column A and a noun from column B to make five sentences that are true for you and your city. Use an adverb of degree in each sentence.**

| A | B |
|---|---|
| clean | park |
| old-fashioned | museums |
| convenient | transportation |
| lively | restaurants |
| attractive | buildings |
| | people |
| | schools |
| | music |

*The museums are really old-fashioned.*

## PRONUNCIATION
### Stress in two-syllable adjectives

2.1 **Underline three more words from the list below that have stress on the second syllable. Then listen and check.**

alive complete direct extreme friendly
happy hungry solid ugly useful

## VOCABULARY
### Verb + preposition

**A Choose the correct preposition to complete each sentence.**

1 When you go out with your best friends, what do you usually talk *about* / *on*?
2 Do you have any friends that you usually argue *about* / *with*?
3 I can't rely *on* / *about* him – he's always late!
4 She needs a lot of help *with* / *on* math. It's not her favorite subject.
5 We're looking *on* / *for* a new house in the city.

**B Complete the text with a verb in the box and a suitable preposition.**

argue looking rely talk talk

My best friend's named Katie. I usually [1]______ ______ her every day on the phone or by email. We [2]______ ______ school or what we're doing on the weekend. I don't really [3]______ ______ her about things because we usually have similar opinions. I haven't called her as much this week because she's so busy. She's [4]______ ______ a job on Saturdays. She doesn't want to [5]______ ______ her parents to give her money.

## PRONUNCIATION
### Consonant pairs at the beginning of words

2.2 **Listen and complete the words with the correct consonant pairs in the box. You will need to use the letters more than once. Then practice saying them aloud to yourself.**

sc sk sl sm sn sp st sw

1 ___eak ___owly
2 ___op ___owing
3 ___eet ___ile
4 ___ow ___art
5 ___art ___imming
6 ___all ___hool
7 ___ake ___in
8 ___ow ___orm

## GRAMMAR
### Simple present and present progressive

**A Look at the pictures and complete the texts using the correct form of a verb in the box.**

have not work pick up play read study take work

Mike's a doctor. Usually, he [1]______ in a hospital. Now, he's on vacation. He [2]______ tennis with his daughter.

Henry's a taxi driver. Usually, he [3]______ people from the airport and [4]______ them into the city. This week, he [5]______. He [6]______ lunch at his favorite restaurant.

Ella and Becky are students. Usually, they [7]______ math. Now, they [8]______ books in the living room.

**B Complete the conversations with the simple present or present progressive form of the verb in parentheses. Use contractions where possible.**

**a Ava:** I hear you [1]______ (*live*) back at your mom and dad's right now.

**Bob:** That's right. I [2]______ (*look for*) a new job with better pay. I [3]______ (*not want*) to live there forever – I need my own place!

**Ava:** Yes, I [4]______ (*know*) what you mean. I [5]______ (*not think*) it's good to rely on your parents too much.

**b Tim:** [6]______ (*do*) Zara ______ (*own*) her house?

**Mia:** No, she doesn't but she really wants to. But house prices [7]______ (*increase*) a lot right now.

**Tim:** It's the same everywhere. I completely [8]______ (*understand*) why people are unhappy.

## GRAMMAR

### Simple past – regular and irregular verbs

**A** Write the simple past form of the following verbs.

1 carry ______
2 come ______
3 give ______
4 have ______
5 like ______
6 make ______
7 play ______
8 plan ______
9 take ______
10 stop ______

**B** Complete the newspaper story with the simple past form of the verb in parentheses. Use contractions where possible.

### Nora's revenge!

Sixty-five-year-old Nora Bentley was angry when a couple bought her house for much less money than she wanted.

Nora [1]______ (*hope*) to sell her house for almost half a million dollars, but Lee and Sarah Boyle [2]______ (*not want*) to spend that much. They [3]______ (*come*) back again and again saying there [4]______ (*be*) problems with the building.

Eventually, they [5]______ (*buy*) the house for $400,000. This was $100,000 less than Nora wanted. Nora [6]______ (*not be*) happy and planned her revenge.

On the day she moved out, Nora [7]______ (*put*) dead fish inside the curtains. Lee and Sarah [8]______ (*notice*) the smell when they first [9]______ (*arrive*) but [10]______ (*not worry*) about it at first. Gradually the smell [11]______ (*get*) worse and worse but Lee and Sarah [12]______ (*cannot*) find the cause. Eventually, they decided to sell the house … for $400,000!

## PRONUNCIATION

### Simple past irregular verbs /ɔː/, /e/ and /eɪ/

2.3 Listen to the phrases below. Decide if the vowel sounds in the verb and the words that follow are the same (S) or different (D). Then practice saying the phrases aloud.

1 I sent a message. S / D
2 Who ate the bread? S / D
3 I slept well. S / D
4 I bought it for my daughter. S / D
5 She said she's twelve. S / D
6 He made his bed. S / D
7 I thought you were Jane. S / D
8 We went ahead. S / D

## VOCABULARY

### Life events

Complete each sentence with a life event in the box below. Make sure you use the correct form of any verbs.

| fall in love | get a job | get married | get my own place | go to college | have children | learn to swim | leave home | leave school | retire |
|---|---|---|---|---|---|---|---|---|---|

1 I'm hoping to ______ at my father's company.
2 My uncle's lucky. He did very well in business and then ______ when he was just forty-five.
3 In my country, people can ______ when they're sixteen but only with their parents' permission. Weddings can be expensive, so usually people wait until they're older.
4 We didn't plan to ______ before we were thirty but we had three! Two boys and a girl.
5 Josie met Alan on vacation and they ______. Now, they're married.
6 She really wants to ______ to study biology next year.
7 Parents usually like their children to be independent but they worry when they ______ and live by themselves.
8 I'm tired of living at home. I want to ______ – maybe a small apartment in the city – as soon as I start earning money.
9 A hundred years ago, education wasn't so good. A lot of children ______ when they were only fourteen.
10 She didn't ______ until she was twenty because she was scared of the water when she was a child.

## READING

**A PREDICT** Read the title and first line of the article. Then choose what you think the article's topic (a–c) is going to be.

- a The worst things about living in the city.
- b The reason for people's accommodation choices.
- c Where the best place to live is.

**B READ FOR MAIN IDEA** Read the article quickly and match the age groups (1–4) to their main priorities (a–d).

| | |
|---|---|
| 1 18–25 | a Living where it's easy to, and close to school or work. |
| 2 26–35 | b Being farther away from cities and towns, but still close to family. |
| 3 36–55 | c Education for their children and the cost of houses. |
| 4 55 + | d Being close to relatives, having a bigger house and more outdoor space. |

**C READ FOR DETAIL** Read the article again. Are the sentences true (T) or false (F)? Correct the false sentences.

1. Most people in their teens and early 20s don't want a lot of things to do where they live. ___
2. People aged 26–35 usually live where they really want to. ___
3. People aged 36–52 usually buy houses where they lived when they were children. ___
4. Most people aged 36–52 enjoy city life. ___
5. People over 55 want the same things as people aged 36–52. ___
6. Most people over 55 don't want to move far away from family. ___

**D REFLECT** Do you think the reasons given in the article for their decisions are correct?

### Glossary

**drawbacks (n)** disadvantages / things you don't like
**priorities (n)** the things you think are most important
**recreational (adj)** done or used for enjoyment
**reputation (n )** the opinion people have about how good or bad something is

## How Do We Choose Where We live?

Why does one person live quietly in the country, another in a small suburban town and another in a huge, noisy city? I frequently look out of a train window and wonder why people live in the various places we pass. Where we live has a constant impact on our lives, so why do we make the choices we make? I decided to find an answer to my question.

Age is important in deciding where we live and how likely we are to move. Most people in their late teens and early 20s live where they grew up. Many still live with their parents and have no choice, but others feel it is important to live close to friends and places of study or work. At this time, many people live where they do simply because it is convenient. They might complain about having no entertainment or recreational facilities, but there are more benefits than drawbacks.

People in their mid-20s to mid-30s are likely to move. They choose to live close to where they or their partner works. They might have a young family and they choose places where schools have a good reputation. House prices are an important consideration, and many in this age group cannot live where they would ideally like to.

People in their mid-30s to early 50s are usually raising a family. They choose to live close to family and friends. Many move back to where they grew up, especially when a larger property is more affordable there. Some people in this age group enjoy city life but most put more emphasis on being close to green space and feeling safe in their environment. People of this age don't mind traveling to a workplace.

People over 55 have different priorities. They usually downsize, selling a large property and buying a smaller one closer to the country. However, people in this age group continue to put importance on living close to family, especially when they have grandchildren.

I'm not sure I have all the answers, but the information helps. When I scan houses from the train window now, I will have a little more of an idea of who lives in each.

## LISTENING

**A PREDICT Look at the picture. What do you think the radio show will be about? Listen to the introduction of the radio show to check your answer.** 2.4

**B LISTEN FOR MAIN IDEA Listen to the introduction again and answer the questions.** 2.4

1 What two types of people does *Houseshare* want to help?
2 Why do some young people need help?
3 Why do some older people need help?

**C Listen to the whole radio show. Decide if the sentences are about young people (Y) or older people (O).** 2.5

1 They are living longer than their parents did. ___
2 Property prices are too high for them. ___
3 They usually have an extra bedroom. ___
4 They don't have a lot of people around to help them. ___
5 They can help by driving. ___
6 They need to answer a lot of questions before doing the project. ___

### Glossary

**companion (n)** someone who is with you
**generation (n)** a group of people in society who are born and live around the same time
**politician (n)** someone who has a job in politics, especially a member of Congress
**proportion (n)** a quantity of something that is part or share of the whole
**reduced (v)** to make something smaller or less in size, amount, importance, etc.
**strict (adj)** someone who is strict has definite rules that they expect people to obey completely

**D REFLECT Think about your answers to these questions.**

1 What do you think about the *Houseshare* project?
2 Is there a similar project in your country? If not, do you think it would be a good idea?

## FUNCTIONAL LANGUAGE
## Ask for and give advice

**Match the sentences (1–8) to the responses (a–h). Then listen to check.** 2.6

1 What should I do? Should I move to New York?
2 Why don't I take care of the kids for you?
3 You could tell Stuart to start exercising.
4 Why don't you ask your parents to help?
5 I think you should try eating at the new restaurant.
6 How about staying with Jill and Martin?
7 There's no cream. What do you suggest?
8 Let me take you to the station.

a No, I can't rely on them all the time.
b Yeah, good idea. They have a spare room.
c How about using milk instead?
d Well, only if you're sure. They're no trouble.
e Well, if you're going that way. Thanks.
f Seriously? Do you think he ever listens to me?
g I'm not sure it's a good idea to leave home so soon.
h Thanks, I'll try it. I really like Thai food.

**a**

Dear Sir/Madam,

___ I was traveling to Columbia from Atlanta and had to change at Charleston. The train from Atlanta was delayed for thirty minutes so when I arrived in Charleston it was too late. The next train to Columbia was then canceled too.

___ In the end, I arrived at the event more than an hour later than I planned. It was a stressful trip and I didn't really enjoy the event.

___ I hope you understand why I am so dissatisfied with the service you provided. I would like the cost of the train ride and the taxi fare to be refunded. I'm looking forward to your reply.

_1_ I am writing to complain about a recent train ride I took with Southways. There was a long delay and I arrived at an important family event much later than planned.

___ I realized I would be late for the event so I decided to take a taxi, which cost $75. It is totally unacceptable that I had to spend this money when I had already paid for my train ride.

Sincerely yours,

Selina Marks

**b**

Dear Sir/Madam,

I am writing to complain about a pair of boots I bought in one of your stores recently. I only wore them three times [1]________ then they broke!

I took them back to the store and spoke to the sales clerk. I asked for a refund [2]________ a replacement [3]________ she didn't help me. She said she couldn't refund or replace them [4]________ it was my fault that they broke. This isn't true – I was only walking in them!

I need these boots for my vacation next month [5]________ I would like you to replace them quickly.

Regards,

Tina Clarke

**c**

[1]**Hello,**

I'm writing about a terrible meal [2]**me and my girlfriend** had at your restaurant on the weekend.

First, we waited forever for a table. [3]**How's** this possible when we made a reservation?

Then we had to wait even longer for the food and then it was disgusting. The pizza was from a grocery store and the salad wasn't fresh.

When the bill came, we complained and asked for a discount. The manager refused.

[4]**Maybe give us back our money**.

[5]**Thanks,**

Max

## WRITING

**A** Read emails (a–c) quickly. Then match them with complaints (1–3).

**1** a bad experience **2** a product **3** a transportation problem

**B** Read email a again. Then number the paragraphs in the correct order.

**C** Read email b again. Then complete the email with the linking words in the box.

and because but or so

**D** Read email c again. Then match words and phrases (1–5) to the reasons (a–e) they are too informal for an email of complaint.

- **a** Greeting too casual ___
- **b** Use of contractions ___
- **c** Incorrect grammar ___
- **d** Sign-off too informal ___
- **e** Language too direct ___

## WRITING PRACTICE

**A PREPARE** You are going to write an email of complaint about something you bought recently. Think about the problem and how you would like the problem to be solved.

**B WRITE** Write your email in 100–150 words.

- Use your notes and ideas from Exercise A.
- Include two or more solutions.
- Use polite and formal language.
- Use linking words.

## GRAMMAR
### *all / some / most / no / none*

**Correct the mistakes in some of the sentences.**

1 Most people I know have a car.

______________________________

2 Some my classmates drive to the college campus.

______________________________

3 There were no parking spaces this morning.

______________________________

4 All of the trains were late this morning.

______________________________

5 No of the buses stopped.

______________________________

6 I spend most my money on traveling to work.

______________________________

7 I wanted some coffee but there was no left.

______________________________

8 All them were late for class.

______________________________

## PRONUNCIATION
### /p/, /b/, /v/

3.1 **Listen to the phrases below and complete the words with *p*, *b* or *v*. Then practice saying them aloud.**

1 ___ack your ___ag
2 a ___ery ___ig ___lane
3 the ___isa is in your ___assport
4 ___isit the ___ort
5 the ___est ___izza in ___enice
6 a ___ery ___ig ___ark in ___arcelona

## VOCABULARY
### Types of transportation

**A Match each description (1–10) with a type of transportation in the box.**

bus (x2) car ferry helicopter minivan motorcycle plane taxi train

1 I like being able to travel from door to door. It's very convenient and I can listen to music. It can be difficult to park in town, though.
2 I don't enjoy it much. The flights are always so full. Also, I get very nervous when we take off and land.
3 It's pretty useful since you can drive to the port and then take your car on. I get a little seasick sometimes though.
4 It's more expensive than taking a bus, but it's usually much quicker. The drivers know the city really well and take you to your exact destination.
5 I bought one when my son started playing soccer because it's a little bigger than our car. I can take him and all his teammates to the games.
6 I've only ever flown in one once. We were in New York and we did a tour over Manhattan. It was expensive but the views were amazing.
7 People ask me how I can travel so far to work every day of my life but it's a routine. I can work on my laptop or talk to other passengers on the trip. I don't need to worry about too much traffic on the roads.
8 There's a stop right outside of my apartment so that's convenient. It only takes about 20 minutes to get to the city.
9 It was a 32-hour trip because of traffic. There were about forty people in the vehicle. It was air conditioned and there was a bathroom.
10 It's definitely more dangerous than driving a car but I love it. I usually take my girlfriend on the back and we head off somewhere nice for the weekend.

**B Circle the correct option in the sentences.**

1 I think we should ***get / travel*** by train. It'll be cheaper than flying.
2 He doesn't want to ***go / get*** a taxi. It's too expensive.
3 Let's ***take a / take*** bus to the city from the airport.
4 I wanted to go ***by a / by*** ferry because I don't like flying.
5 My dad ***flew / flight*** to meet me in Paris last year because it was the quickest way to get there.

## GRAMMAR
### Past progressive and simple past

**A** Choose the correct verb forms in the sentences below.

1 *Did they enjoy* / *Were they enjoying* their vacation? They came home yesterday, didn't they?

2 He *was sleeping* / *slept* at 4 am when his car was stolen.

3 We *didn't take* / *weren't taking* the ferry because there was a bad storm.

4 *Were you living* / *Did you live* in your hometown in 2008?

5 They *started* / *were starting* college in 2014 and they graduated in 2018.

**B** Read the postcard below. Then complete it with the correct form of the verb provided.

**POSTCARD**

| THIS SPACE FOR WRITING MESSAGE | FOR ADDRESS ONLY |
|---|---|
| Hey Tom!<br>I'm having a fun time on my trip, but something scary happened last week.<br>I [1] ______________ (*travel*) in Vietnam with a group of people. We [2] ______________ (*walk*) through the forest when suddenly the guide [3] ______________ (*yell*). He [4] ______________ (*not speak*) English so we [5] ______________ (*run*) to see what the problem was. We [6] ______________ (*see*) a huge snake. It was about three meters long. My heart [7] ______________ (*beat*) really fast when the guide [8] ______________ (*pick*) it up and [9] ______________ (*move*) it into the trees.<br>Looking forward to seeing you soon!<br>Mike | Tom Morris<br>21 Elmlea Street<br>New York, NY |

**C** Complete the sentences below with *when* or *while* and the past progressive or simple past form of the verbs in parentheses.

1 I read my book ______________ I ______________ (*wait*) for the bus.

2 I was swimming in the ocean, ______________ I ______________ (*lose*) my car keys.

3 He was listening to music ______________ he ______________ (*drive*) his new car.

4 I didn't recognize Anne ______________ she ______________ (*say*) *hello* to me on the street.

5 ______________ they ______________ (*talk*), the doorbell rang.

## PRONUNCIATION
### *was* and *were* with past progressive

3.2 **When people speak quickly, *is* and *was* and *are* and *were* sound very similar. Listen and underline the sentence or question you hear. Then practice saying them.**

1 We're playing chess. / We were playing chess.

2 Is she going? / Was she going?

3 What are they doing? / What were they doing?

4 Is he living in Brooklyn? / Was he living in Brooklyn?

5 Where are you going? / Where were you going?

## VOCABULARY
### Prefixes

**A** Complete the descriptions (1–7) below using a negative form of an adjective in the box.

correct healthy honest lucky patient possible usual

1 Zoe never tells the truth. I can't believe a word she says. She's ______________.

2 I'm afraid this answer isn't right. It's ______________.

3 It's like teaching a fish to ride a bicycle. It just can't be done! It's ______________.

4 I like the name Esmerelda. Not many people have that name. It's ______________.

5 Tony wants everything done now. He won't wait ten minutes. He's ______________.

6 Every time I go on vacation, it rains. I'm ______________.

7 Jimmy eats fries, fries and more fries! He's really ______________.

**B** Add the correct prefix *un-*, *im-*, *dis-* or *in-* to the adjectives (1–7) in the sentence beginnings. Then match them to the sentence endings (a–g).

1 He's ___happy

2 She's ___polite

3 They're ___organized

4 The article is ___accurate

5 The man was ___kind

6 It's ___likely

7 She was so ___friendly

a because she never says *please* or *thank you*.

b because the reporter got the dates wrong.

c because he failed his driving test.

d because he didn't help the old lady carry her bags.

e that it will snow in May.

f because they never plan anything properly.

g because she didn't smile or say *hello*.

## GRAMMAR
### verb + *-ing* and *to* + base form

**A** Read the phone conversation carefully. Find and correct the six mistakes.

**Jackie:** Hi, Mark. Are you ready for tomorrow?
**Mark:** Hi, Jackie. I'm just packing now.
**Jackie:** Remember packing your iPad. Mine's not working.
**Mark:** Yes, I've done that. Anyway, what time should we take the train to the airport?
**Jackie:** We don't need worrying about that. My dad's agreed to give us a ride.
**Mark:** Are you sure?
**Jackie:** It's fine. Dad doesn't mind to drive.
**Mark:** What time do we need leaving in the morning?
**Jackie:** At 8:30.
**Mark:** That's really early ...
**Jackie:** Yes, I know. I want to spend time to shop.
**Mark:** Yes, good idea. I need to exchange some money. I didn't manage getting to the bank this afternoon.
**Jackie:** OK. I'm going to finish to pack now. Bye!

**B** Rewrite the sentences below using a verb + *-ing* or *to* + base form.

1 I like to go out with Tim and Suzy.
I always enjoy ______.
2 Renting a car costs too much money.
We can't afford ______.
3 I'll give you this book when I've read it.
I'll give you this book when I finish ______.
4 We played more tennis after our friend went home.
We continued ______.
5 Jill said that she wouldn't give me the money.
Jill refused ______.

## VOCABULARY
### Accommodations and amenities

**A** Match the sentence halves.

1 The Spanish coast has many beach
2 You should book a single or double
3 I'm going to order a sandwich from room
4 They stayed at a guest
5 We had an amazing ocean
6 We booked a self-service
7 I need to arrange an airport
8 I've never traveled on a huge cruise
9 We stayed in a beautiful 5-star
10 We stayed at a youth

a service.
b house.
c view.
d transfer.
e room.
f resorts.
g hostel.
h hotel.
i apartment.
j ship.

**B** Read the clues and complete the crossword.

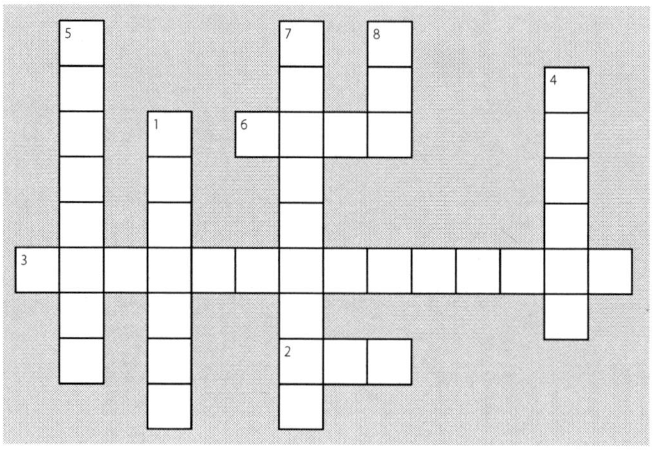

Across
2 where guests can relax and possibly have a massage
3 keeps rooms cool in summer
6 a large shared room in a hostel

Down
1 where guests can sit outside and enjoy the views
4 vacation home for skiers
5 a place to pitch tents
7 where guests check in and out
8 where guests can work out to keep fit, or stay in shape

## PRONUNCIATION
### /ʃ/, /tʃ/ and /dʒ/

3.3 Write the words shown in phonetics below. Listen to check. Then practice saying each word out loud.

1 /tʃu:z/ ______
2 /ˈdʒenju:wɪn/ ______
3 /ˈʃæleɪ/ ______
4 /ˈpɪktʃər/ ______
5 /tʃeɪndʒ/ ______

## READING

**A PREDICT** Look at the extracts (1–6) quickly. Then match them to the text types (a–f).

| | | | |
|---|---|---|---|
| **a** a travel blog | ___ | **d** a review | ___ |
| **b** a news report | ___ | **e** a travel guide | ___ |
| **c** a postcard | ___ | **f** an email of complaint | ___ |

**B IDENTIFY TONE** Read the extracts again and decide if they are formal (F) or informal (I).

**1** ___ **2** ___ **3** ___ **4** ___ **5** ___ **6** ___

**1**

Trains are a good way to travel in the US. They connect major towns and cities, are fast and comfortable, and trips are direct. If you are traveling to more remote towns, you will probably need to change trains.

Train fares in the US are not cheap, but there are discounts for students and older travelers. You can buy tickets at train stations or book online. Some routes are very busy, so it is advisable to book a seat before you travel.

**2**

**POSTCARD**

THIS SPACE FOR WRITING MESSAGE

*Hi Marcus and Cath,*

*Luxor is a fantastic city! It's very hot and very noisy but really interesting. We visited some temples today and tomorrow we're going to take a boat trip up the Nile!! Our hotel has two pools and four restaurants. The food here is delicious!*

*Paula XXX*

**3**

So, do I have a problem with package tourism? Yes! Tourists on package vacations have zero interest in the culture of the country they visit. They just want photos to share online with their friends and a suntan. I mean, where's the adventure in eating all your meals in your hotel? Don't people want to learn something new when they travel?

**4**

The government hopes that a new runway at Heathrow Airport will be opening soon. Politicians say that the UK depends on Heathrow Airport as a connection to the world economy. They believe it will lose its status as a major global airport if it does not expand …

**5**

I am writing about a flight to Turkey that was delayed for over seven hours. It was flight TK115. It was due to leave New York at 2:20 pm but finally left at 9:35 pm.

I asked the check-in manager for an explanation, but he was very unhelpful. He clearly had no wish to …

**6**

Overall, we enjoyed our stay in *Hotel Las Flores*. It is very central and very close to a subway station. We had a room with an ocean view. It was spacious and nicely decorated. The hotel staff was so friendly … ★★★★☆

**C SCAN** Read the texts again. Are the sentences true (T) or false (F)? Correct the false sentences.

1. Passengers usually need to change trains on trips between two big cities. *T / F*
2. Some people pay less than others on trains. *T / F*
3. Paula went on a boat yesterday. *T / F*
4. Paula is staying in a small hotel. *T / F*
5. The blog writer likes package vacations. *T / F*
6. The blog writer thinks people who go on package vacations are interested in culture. *T / F*
7. The government wants Heathrow Airport to be bigger. *T / F*
8. The flight from New York to Turkey left very late. *T / F*
9. The check-in manager at the airport helped the traveler. *T / F*
10. The hotel reviewer was happy with the location of the hotel. *T / F*

**D REFLECT** Think about your answers to these questions.

1. Do you think tourists on package vacations learn about other cultures?
2. Should the traveler to Turkey get a refund?

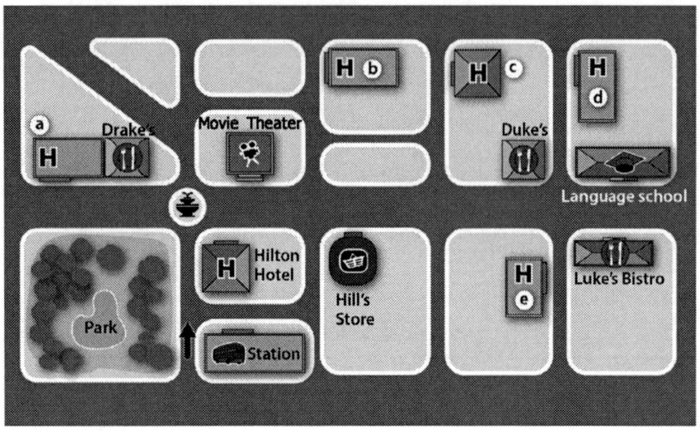


## LISTENING

**A PREDICT** Look at the map above. Think about the directions you would give from the station to each of the hotels (a–e).

3.4 **B** Look at the map again and listen to a man giving some tourists directions. Which hotel (a–e) do the tourists want to go to?

3.5 **C LISTEN FOR DETAIL** Listen to the second part of the conversation. Complete the information below.

| | | |
|---|---|---|
| Duration of walk to hotel | : | 1 ______ |
| Number of bus | : | 2 ______ |
| Duration of bus trip | : | 3 ______ |
| Cost of single bus trip | : | 4 $___ |
| Cost of taxi | : | 5 $___ |

**D** Listen to the second part of the conversation again and choose the correct answer (a or b).

1 The tourists' luggage ___ weigh a lot.
a does b doesn't

2 There are a lot of ___ on Station Road.
a bus stops b cars

3 The man thinks the bus is ___ expensive.
a really b fairly

4 The taxi takes ___ time than the bus.
a less b more

5 The tourists decide to ___.
a walk b go by taxi

### Glossary

**fairly (adv)** to some degree, but not extremely or completely

**fountain (n)** a structure through which a stream of water is pumped into the air and falls down again

**E REFLECT** Think about your answers to these questions.

1 When you are in a new city, do you prefer to ask someone for directions or use a map?

2 Do you prefer to walk or use public transportation in a new city?

## FUNCTIONAL LANGUAGE

### Ask for travel information and check understanding

3.6 **A** Complete each conversation with one verb. Then listen to check.

1 **A:** That bag looks heavy. Let me ______ you with it.
**B:** No, don't ______, I can manage.

2 **A:** Here, don't ______ your cell phone.
**B:** Oh, thanks. I'd be lost without it.

3 **A:** Which way's platform 3?
**B:** I'm going that way too, ______ me.

4 **A:** Do I have to ______ trains on this trip?
**B:** No, this one's direct.

5 **A:** Is that the train I want on platform 2?
**B:** Yes, hurry up. It leaves in two minutes. You don't want to ______ it.

6 **A:** What time does the train ______ in the city?
**B:** At 2:35.

**B** Complete each phrase with the correct preposition.

1 ___ 3:40 pm
2 arrive ___ Paris
3 arrive ___ the station
4 get ___ Dublin
5 a one-way ___ New York
6 leaving ___ about ten minutes
7 leaving ___ platform 3
8 change ___ Penn Station
9 go straight ___

# 3.6 Travel

Write an email about a travel experience

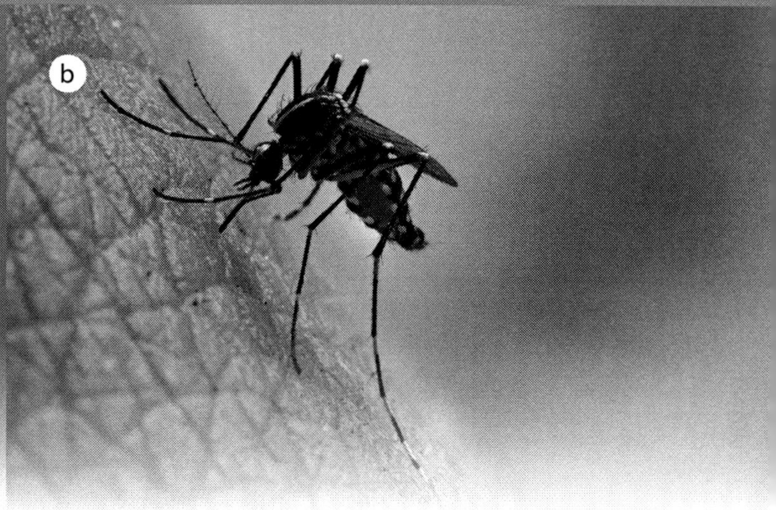


## WRITING

**A** Complete the words and phrases (1–4) with the correct vowels. Then match them to the correct picture (a–d).

**1** s___nb___rn ___
**2** f___ ___d p___ ___s___n___ng ___
**3** ___ns___ct b___t___ ___
**4** d___l___y___d fl___ght ___

**B** Read Caterina's email. Which two problems from Exercise A does she mention?

**To:** Maria
**From:** Caterina
**Subject:** Vacation update!

Hi Maria,

How are you? All is going well in Greece now, but I was fairly unlucky during the first few days. [1]___________, I forgot to use sunblock and it was such a hot day that I got a sunburn. It was really painful when I went to bed. [2]___________ when I woke up it didn't hurt as much, so I bought some sunscreen and went sightseeing. While I was walking around the Acropolis, I got a little hungry so I bought an ice-cream cone from a store. [3]A few ___________ later, at about 5 pm, I started to feel a little sick. I needed to call the doctor, who came quickly and gave me some medicine. [4]___________ taking the medicine, I felt a lot better and [5]___________ I could start to enjoy the vacation!

A lot of good things happened yesterday, thankfully! For example, I met a really nice woman who knows a lot about the history and culture of the island. She took me to a restaurant that serves traditional Greek food – it was delicious. I hope my last few days will be fun and without any more bad luck!

Talk to you soon!

Caterina xx

**C** Complete Caterina's email with the words or phrases in the box.

| after | first | hours | the next day | then |
|---|---|---|---|---|

## WRITING PRACTICE

**A PREPARE** You are going to write an email to a friend about a travel experience. Write a plan and think about the following:

- Whether you will write about a good or bad experience.
- What happened and how to use the language from Writing Exercise A if necessary.
- How to use the language from Writing Exercise C to say the order things happened in.

**B WRITE** Write your email in 100–150 words.

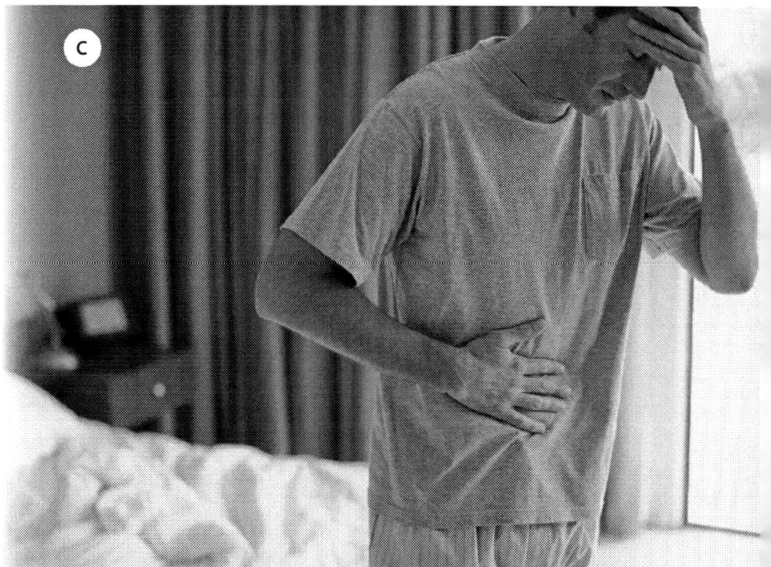

## VOCABULARY
### Free time

**A** Complete the email with the correct form of a phrase in the box. You may use each phrase more than once.

go for   go to   hang out with   play

Hi Christine,

We had a great time in Spain. The apartment was great and we spent a lot of time together as a family – well we tried to anyway. Jason and Suzy enjoyed [1] __________ some kids that were staying in the apartment next to ours. They all got along really well. Now that Debbie's eighteen she loves dancing so all she wanted to do was [2] __________ nightclubs. She didn't come back until 3 am most nights! We wanted the kids [3] __________ board games in the evening with us – but they were both too busy on their tablets. At least we all ate together. We loved the food and we [4] __________ a delicious meal in a local restaurant one evening. We spent most days lying on the beach but we [5] __________ an exhibit of local art one afternoon – the kids were bored, naturally! On the last day, we all [6] __________ a long bike ride. We biked about 10 km – everyone was exhausted.

See you soon!

Gemma XXX

**B** Correct the mistakes with prepositions in each of the sentences.

1 I'm going to take my wife to a nice Japanese meal.
2 We went in an amazing Picasso exhibit on the weekend.
3 A lot of teenagers hang out by their friends.
4 I'm going out at coffee with Jane. Do you want to come?
5 I'd like to see to a movie this evening. What do you think?
6 I usually take my kids to play to the park after school.
7 I'm tired. I've just been to a long jog.
8 I usually play about cards with my mom and dad after dinner.

## GRAMMAR
### *be going to* + base form and present progressive for the future

**A** James and Tina have just won the lottery and they have big plans. Complete the sentences using the correct form of *be going to* and a verb in the box.

buy   give   give up   not move   paint   travel

1 They __________ their jobs.
2 They __________ around the world.
3 James __________ a Ferrari.
4 Tina __________ pictures in her studio all day.
5 They __________ money to their families.
6 They __________ to a bigger house.

**B** Answer the questions below about James and Tina using short answers. Use contractions where possible.

1 Are they going to stop working? __________
2 Are they going to travel? __________
3 Is James going to buy a Porsche? __________
4 Is Tina going to do some art? __________
5 Are they going to keep all their money? __________
6 Are they going to stay in the same house? __________

**C** Choose the correct future form in each sentence in the conversation below.

**Doug:** [1]*Are you doing / Are you going to do* anything on Monday?
**Geoff:** On Monday, [2]*I'm going to take / I'm taking* my son to his first soccer game … Arsenal and City.
**Doug:** Lucky you. What about Tuesday?
**Geoff:** It's my wedding anniversary. [3]*We're going to meet / We're meeting* our friends Ella and Ray for dinner.
**Doug:** And I guess you have something on Wednesday?
**Geoff:** Yes, how did you know? I bought a TV last week but it doesn't work properly. [4]*I'm going to take / I'm taking* it back to see if they can change it.
**Doug:** It sounds as if you're really busy.
**Geoff:** Yes, I am right now. On Thursday, I have to give my neighbors a ride to the airport. [5]*They're going to fly / They're flying* out to Spain for a week. I might be able to meet on Friday, though.
**Doug:** I can't. My favorite movie's on TV and [6]*I'm going to watch / I'm watching* it for the fifteenth time!

## PRONUNCIATION
### *going to*

4.1 Listen and write down exactly what you hear.

1 __________
2 __________
3 __________

## GRAMMAR
### Making predictions

**A** Complete each second sentence using the word given so it has a similar meaning to the first sentence.

1 It's fairly likely that Jenny is coming to the party.
**WILL**
Jenny ______________________
to the party.

2 Humans living on Mars in five years just isn't going to happen.
**BE**
Humans ______________________
on Mars in five years.

3 I'm fairly sure James will be late.
**PROBABLY**
James ______________________ be on time.

4 I'm sure that Lara's going to be the winner of the game.
**DEFINITELY**
Lara ______________________
the game.

**B** Find and correct the mistakes in some of the sentences.

1 We'll come definitely to the beach barbecue on Sunday.
______________________

2 There won't certainly be paper money in the future.
______________________

3 Maybe Jim will help us with the arrangements.
______________________

4 Edward said that he probably won't be able to get a ticket for the concert.
______________________

5 Cities in the future probably will look very different.
______________________

## PRONUNCIATION
### *will* and *won't*

4.2 Listen and underline the phrase you hear. Then practice saying the future forms to yourself.

| | a | b |
|---|---|---|
| 1 | we go | we'll go |
| 2 | I come | I'll come |
| 3 | they do | they'll do |
| 4 | you like | you'll like |
| 5 | we buy | we'll buy |
| 6 | she has | she'll have |

## VOCABULARY
### Suffixes

Use the suffixes in the box to create nouns from the words in 1–5. The same suffix is required for three of the four words in each group. One word in each group requires a different suffix.

-ation -ion -ity -ment -ness

| | | | | |
|---|---|---|---|---|
| 1 | agree | discuss | improve | develop |
| 2 | able | possible | real | weak |
| 3 | happy | sad | active | lonely |
| 4 | relax | explain | react | occupy |
| 5 | enjoy | predict | ambitious | create |

## GRAMMAR
### Subject and object questions

**A** Use the prompts to write subject or object questions. Use the answers to the questions to help you.

1 Bill Gates / become / rich?

_______________

He founded Microsoft.

2 become / President of the US / 2008?

_______________

Barack Obama.

3 Vikings / come from?

_______________

They came from Scandinavia.

4 Mexicans / celebrate / Day of the Dead?

_______________

They celebrate it from October 31st to November 2nd.

5 reggae musician / die / 1981?

_______________

Bob Marley.

**B** Correct the mistakes.

1 What gave you Sarah for a birthday present?

_______________

2 Who did John win the game?

_______________

3 How she find the station?

_______________

4 Whose bicycle stole the thieves?

_______________

## VOCABULARY
### Relaxing

**A** Match the sentence halves to make adjective-noun collocations.

1 You need to enjoy the **simple**
2 Have a **quiet**
3 Enjoy some **homemade**
4 Create a **relaxed**
5 Run yourself a **hot**
6 Listen to **soft**

a **atmosphere** with candles and soft music.
b **bath**.
c **things** in life.
d **food** and something nice to drink.
e **music** as you think.
f **night** in watching your favorite TV show.

**B** Match the sentence halves to make verb/noun collocations.

1 You need to work less and **take**
2 Everyone loves **reading**
3 You can **play**
4 It's nice to **sit**
5 You can **light**
6 It's great to **get together with**
7 When you get home, **take**

a **by the fire** and drink hot chocolate.
b **friends and family**.
c **a good book** by a warm fire.
d **some time out** to relax.
e **a hot bath** and completely relax.
f **board games** with your kids.
g **some candles** to create the right atmosphere.

## PRONUNCIATION
### Linking a consonant to a vowel

4.3 Listen and write the two words that you hear. Then practice saying each phrase to yourself.

1 _______________
2 _______________
3 _______________
4 _______________
5 _______________
6 _______________

## READING

**A PREDICT** Look at the title of the article and the pictures. What information do you think will be given in the article? Quickly read the article to check your answer.

**B READ FOR MAIN IDEA** Four sentences have been removed from the article. Choose which sentence (a–d) fits each blank (1–4).

- **a** Years later, when the participants were in their fifties, they were asked questions about their social lives.
- **b** With this information, doctors might be able to identify individuals who are more likely to suffer from loneliness in the future.
- **c** We need a circle of close friends who we can trust and rely on.
- **d** We spend less time with the people we really care about.

**C READ FOR DETAIL** Read the article again and complete each paragraph summary with words in the box.

| because | closer | develop | every | guess | more | opposite | priority | research | showed | young |
|---|---|---|---|---|---|---|---|---|---|---|

**Introduction:** Scientists say relationships [1]________ as we age.

**Paragraph 1:** When we are [2]________ the number of friends we have is important. As we get older, [3]________ relationships are a [4]________.

**Paragraph 2:** In the 1970s, scientists did some [5]________ on people at different points in their lives about their interactions [6]________ day.

**Paragraph 3:** The study [7]________ the happiest people had [8]________ friends at twenty and fewer closer friends at thirty. Participants with the [9]________ situation were more lonely. This could be [10]________ having too many friends in your thirties makes life more difficult.

**Paragraph 4:** Doctors are looking at friendships when people are younger to [11]________ how happy people will be when they're older.

**D REFLECT** Think about your answers to these questions.

1. Do you think the information given in the text is totally true, partly true or totally untrue?
2. Do you think that a study with one hundred participants can give accurate results?

## How We Socialize Might Shape Our Future

***Scientists have discovered some interesting information about how we view relationships. As we get older, the way we think about friendship changes.***

When we are in high school and college, quantity of friends is more important. The more friends we have, the happier we are. We feel we are popular and successful socially. We want to learn as much as we can about as many people as possible. As we grow up, quality becomes more important and we look for more intimate relationships with a smaller number of people. [1]___

In the 1970s, a thirty-year study on one hundred American students began. At the age of twenty and then again at the age of thirty, each student made brief notes about all of their daily social interactions. They noted how long each interaction lasted and how it made them feel. [2]___

The study found that participants who had a large number of friends at twenty and a smaller, closer circle of friends at thirty were the happiest. Participants who had fewer friends at twenty and a wider, less intimate circle of friends at thirty were more likely to be lonely. One possible conclusion is that having too many friends in our thirties complicates life.[3]___

Now, doctors claim that they can predict how happy people will be in their old age by studying their friendships earlier in their lives.[4]___

### Glossary

**complicate (v)** make something more difficult to do or understand
**interaction (n)** being with and talking to other people
**participants (n)** people who take part in an activity (here, in a study)
**popular (adj)** liked by a lot of people

# 4.5 Socializing

Listening; Functional Language

## LISTENING

**A PREDICT** **You will hear speakers (1–5) making predictions about the future. Match each speaker to which prediction (a–e) you think they are likely to make.**

| | | |
|---|---|---|
| **Speaker 1** | a medical student | ___ |
| **Speaker 2** | a college lecturer | ___ |
| **Speaker 3** | an architect | ___ |
| **Speaker 4** | an aid worker | ___ |
| **Speaker 5** | a media studies student | ___ |

**a** Our homes will be very different.

**b** The way we speak to each other might change a lot.

**c** An aging population might really change higher education.

**d** There will be even larger poor areas in urban areas.

**e** An aging population will put a huge strain on healthcare.

4.4 **B LISTEN FOR MAIN IDEA** **Listen to check your answers in Exercise A.**

**Glossary**

**aggressive (adj)** behaving in an angry or rude way that shows you want to fight, attack or argue with someone
**anonymous (adj)** if someone is anonymous, no one knows their name
**impact (n)** an effect or an influence
**sustainable (adj)** using methods that do not harm the environment

4.4 **C LISTEN FOR DETAIL** **Listen again. Complete the summaries with a word in the box.**

> adult age buildings change cost crime different leave old poor young

Speaker 1 says that in some places there will be more [1]___ people than [2]___ people. She is worried about the rising [3]___ of healthcare.

Speaker 2 says that the average [4]___ of students might rise and that there will be a more [5]___ way of life in college.

Speaker 3 says that people will live in very tall [6]___ that are like towns within cities. People will have everything they need nearby and will rarely need to [7]___.

Speaker 4 says that [8]___ people will not live in modern buildings. Millions will live in huge shanty towns where there may be a lot of [9]___.

Speaker 5 says that the way people communicate face-to-face and online is very [10]___. He is worried that the internet will [11]___ the way people speak forever.

**D REFLECT** **Think about which of the speakers you most agree and disagree with.**

## FUNCTIONAL LANGUAGE

### Make arrangements to meet up with somebody

4.5 **Choose the correct options to complete the conversations. Then listen to check.**

**1 Emily:** Do you [1]*want / like* to eat out this evening?
**Maria:** Yeah, [2]*I'd love to / I want to.* [3]*Could / Will* we try that new Korean place by the bus station?
**Emily:** Yes, [4]*looks good / sounds great.*
**Maria:** Oh, [5]*wait a minute / not really.* I just remembered that my sister's coming over. She wants to talk about Mom and Dad's anniversary.
**Emily:** Well, that's OK. You can talk about it and then we'll go out for dinner.

**2 Greg:** Hi Dave, it's me … Greg. [6]*Do you / Are you* free on Saturday night?
**Dave:** I'm not sure. I'll just check my calendar. Um. Yes, I'm [7]*leaving / free.* Did you want to meet for a drink or something?
**Greg:** Actually, I'm hoping you [8]*are / could* babysit. Emma and I are going to the theater.
**Dave:** Yeah, OK then. What time?
**Greg:** Could you be here at 7:30?
**Dave:** I'm so [9]*sorry / worried* – I can't do that time because I'll be at my Spanish class until 8:00. How [10]*maybe / about* 8:15?
**Greg:** Great, 8:15 [11]*it is / is it.*

# 4.6 Socializing Write an invitation

## WRITING

**A** Imagine that you want to invite a friend from another country to your town or city. Answer the questions below.

1. When is the best time to visit?
2. What sights would you take him/her to see?
3. Are there any museums or galleries he/she should visit?
4. Are there any national or local festivals that he/she would enjoy?

**B** Read Caroline's email below and underline the things she wants to do when Lorena comes to visit.

To: Lorena
From: Caroline
Subject: Come and see me!

Hi Lorena,

[1]__________ I hope you're not studying too hard! It seems a long time ago that I was in Madrid. I'd love to see you again – which is why I'm emailing. [2]__________ the last weekend in June? My exams finish on August 25th, so I would like to invite you to London for a few days to stay. [3]__________ I really hope so!

It would be a great time to visit because it's the weekend of the Notting Hill Carnival. It's a celebration of the British West Indian community. The Notting Hill area is one big party for three days!

There are huge parades and the streets are crowded. Everywhere, you can buy delicious West Indian food. We could also go to see Big Ben and hang out in Regent's Park. Maybe even go to the theater to see a show.

Anyway [4]__________ so I can start making plans for other places we can go.

[5]__________

[6]__________

Caroline

**C** Read Caroline's email again and complete 1–6 with the informal phrases (a–f).

a. Bye for now!
b. Let me know if you're coming
c. How's life?
d. I hope you can make it.
e. Do you have any plans for
f. Would you like to come?

**D** Read Lorena's reply below. Put the paragraphs into the correct order.

To: Caroline
From: Lorena
Subject: RE: Come and see me!

Hi Caroline

__ I'd love to come, but unfortunately I can't make it.

__ Great to hear from you! Yes, our time in Madrid was so long ago!

__ Thank you so much for inviting me to London. It's a great idea and I have always wanted to visit.

__ August is going to be very busy for me because I am going on vacation with my family. I also have to work on the weekends.

__ See you soon!

__ I'm going to have a lot more free time in September, so maybe I could come to London then. I'll miss the Notting Hill Carnival, but we could go to Madame Tussauds or the London Eye instead?

Lorena

## WRITING PRACTICE

**A PREPARE** You are going to write an email to a friend from another country inviting him or her to visit you.

- Decide which friend (real or imaginary) you are going to invite to your country.
- Decide which of your ideas from Writing Exercise A you will use.

**B WRITE** Write your email in 100 words. Remember to use informal language.

## GRAMMAR
### *can, could, be able to*

**A** Match the sentence halves using *because* or *but*.

1 Jason wants to be a taxi driver
2 Sarah hopes to be a translator
3 My mom wanted to be a doctor
4 Tim would love to be a lifeguard
5 Sally wanted to be an accountant
6 Sam wants to become a comedian
7 George wanted to be an artist
8 Zoe knew she could be a pop star

**because**
**but**

a he could paint and draw so well.
b she could sing so beautifully.
c he can't drive.
d she couldn't stand the sight of blood.
e she can speak five languages.
f he can't swim.
g he can make everyone laugh.
h she couldn't do math.

**B** Correct the mistakes in some of the sentences.

1 I live on the coast and I can walking on the beach every day.

____________________________________

2 Fortunately, we were able to park outside their house.

____________________________________

3 Sam locked himself out of the house, but he could to get through a downstairs window.

____________________________________

4 The earliest computers wasn't able to do complicated things like modern computers.

____________________________________

5 I couldn't speak to my wife on the phone but I could text her.

____________________________________

6 Can you speak any English when you were eleven?

____________________________________

**C** Rewrite the sentences using the correct form of *be able to*. Use contractions where possible.

1 Sorry, we can't take your call right now.
Sorry, we ____________ take your call right now.

2 Can you get to the meeting by 10:30?
____________ get to the meeting by 10:30?

3 It was easy to get tickets for the show.
We ____________ get tickets for the show fairly easily.

4 It's great that we can watch so many TV channels nowadays.
People enjoy ____________ watch so many TV channels nowadays.

## VOCABULARY
### Work collocations

**A** Correct the second word in each collocation in bold.

1 Most doctors work very **long skills** and they're always on call.
2 Most people working in fast food restaurants earn a **low shift**.
3 If I get a **pay wage** next year, I'm going to buy a new car.
4 Monday is a bank holiday, so we get an **extra raise** off this week.
5 People are usually paid a little better if they have **special hours** and abilities.
6 I get a **company day** at my new job. I'll probably choose a Volkswagen Golf.

**B** Complete the sentences with the correct verb in the box.

be earn get get take work

1 It's my son's birthday tomorrow. I'm going to ____________ the day off and we're going to the zoo.
2 Doctors ____________ very long hours. A fourteen-hour shift is pretty usual.
3 Most people who work in fast food restaurants ____________ a low salary.
4 My brother had a job until last month but he ____________ unemployed now.
5 I make $300 a week but I'm hoping to ____________ a pay raise soon.
6 I hope we ____________ a bonus this year.

## PRONUNCIATION
### /w/ and /v/

5.1 Listen and write down the phrases.

1 ____________
2 ____________
3 ____________
4 ____________
5 ____________
6 ____________

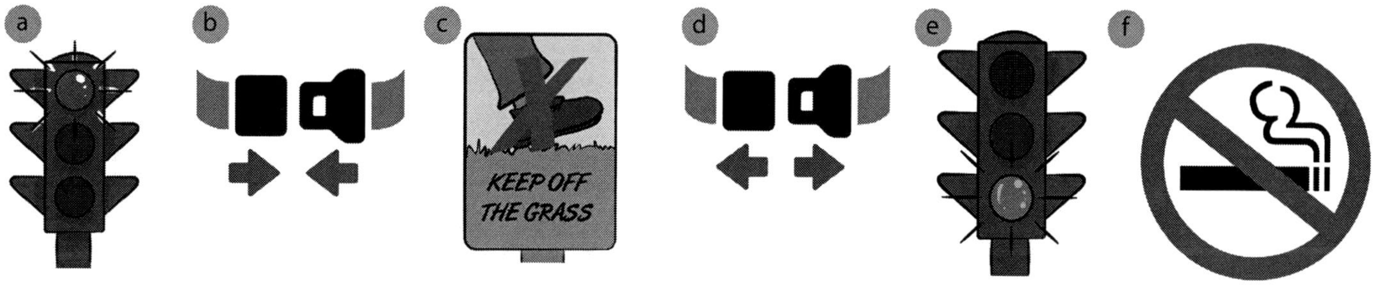


## GRAMMAR
### Obligation, necessity and permission: *must*, *have to* and *can*

**A** Match signs (a–f) with sentences (1–6). Then complete each sentence with *must*, *must not* or *can*.

1 You ________ fasten your seatbelt. ___
2 You ________ smoke anywhere in the building. ___
3 You ________ go now – the light is green and the cars behind us are waiting! ___
4 You ________ walk on the grass. ___
5 You ________ unfasten your seatbelt, if you want to. ___
6 You ________ stop when the light is red. ___

**B** Complete the conversation using *can*, *can't*, *have to* or *don't have to*.

**Uncle:** So Leo, do you [1] ________________ wear a uniform?

**Nephew:** We [2] ________________ wear a uniform from Monday to Thursday, but we [3] ________________ wear it on Friday. We [4] ________________ wear casual clothes on Friday, but some people choose to wear their uniform.

**Uncle:** Do you like your teacher?

**Nephew:** Yes, but we [5] ________________ talk when she's talking. We [6] ________________ listen.

**Uncle:** Well, that's good, isn't it? It's polite.

**Nephew:** I guess so. We all [7] ________________ stand up when she enters the classroom – it's a school rule. Then she takes the attendance and one student [8] ________________ take the attendance to the school's office.

## PRONUNCIATION
### *can* / *can't* and *must* / *must not*

5.2 Listen and circle the phrase that you hear.

1 *can be / can't be*
2 *must go / must not go*
3 *must take / must not take*
4 *can do / can't do*

## VOCABULARY
### Adjectives for appearance

**Choose the correct adjectives to complete the description.**

It was my older sister's wedding last week. Almost all the men were wearing suits and they looked very [1]*nice / colorful*. Since it was a really hot day, most of the women were in [2]*attractive / cool* dresses. My dad was wearing a vest under his suit, which he thinks is very [3]*fashionable / casual* right now because he saw an actor on TV wearing one! My mom looked very [4]*stylish / colorful* in a simple gray pantsuit. My younger brother decided not to wear a suit because he wanted to look more [5]*casual / nice*. He was wearing a bright green shirt and dark jeans. He wore his sunglasses all day, which he thought looked [6]*cool / colorful*. Everyone else thought he looked ridiculous!

## GRAMMAR

### Present perfect with *for* and *since*

**A** Complete the article with the present perfect or simple past forms of the verbs in parentheses and circle *for* or *since*.

# Take me on.

If a big company [1] ________ (*ask*) you to attend a job interview, stay calm. Check our expert advice from Karen Johnson at The Job Center. It tells you how to prepare and what to do if you say the wrong thing.

**Find out as much as you can before the interview.**

I interview a lot of people, and many of them clearly [2] ________ (*not think*) about the job [3] ***for / since*** they [4] ________ (*send*) their résumé. Do some research so you can explain why you want THIS job with THIS company.

**Make sure you can explain any time when you were unemployed.**

If you [5] ________ (*not work*) [6] ***for / since*** a long time, explain why. Say what you [7] ________ (*spend*) your time doing [8] ***for / since*** you last [9] ________ (*have*) a job. [10] ________ you ________ (*study*) or ________ (*travel*) since you had a job?

**People frequently say the wrong thing when they are nervous.**

I [11] ________ (*work*) in my job [12] ***for / since*** 2008, and I [13] ________ (*be*) to a lot of job interviews. I understand why people get nervous and make mistakes when they speak. If you say the wrong thing, admit that you [14] ________ (*be*) wrong and start again.

**B** Match the beginning of a question (1–6) with the end of a question (a–f). Then answer each question using either *for* or *since*.

1 How long have you known
2 How long have you had
3 How long have you lived
4 How long have you studied
5 How long have you been
6 How long have you supported

a your favorite pair of shoes?
b English?
c your best friend?
d your favorite soccer team?
e in your city?
f doing your hobby?

1 ________
2 ________
3 ________
4 ________
5 ________
6 ________

## PRONUNCIATION

### *has, have, for, since*

5.3 Listen and write the sentences exactly as your hear them.

1 ________
2 ________
3 ________
4 ________
5 ________

## VOCABULARY

### *work* + preposition

**A** Complete the sentences using *in*, *for* or *at*.

1 Models usually work ____ the fashion industry.
2 Waiters usually work ____ restaurants.
3 Car mechanics can work ____ BMW.
4 Flight attendants usually work ____ international airlines.
5 Aid workers usually work ____ the nonprofit sector.
6 Taxi drivers usually work ____ small local firms.
7 Nurses usually work ____ hospitals.

**B** Complete the sentences using *in*, *for* or *at*.

# Before they were famous

1 Kanye West used to work ________ a Gap store.
2 Mariah Carey worked ________ a hairdresser who owned a local salon.
3 Back in Hawaii, Barack Obama was employed ________ an ice cream company.
4 Lady Gaga was a waitress ________ a downtown Greek restaurant.
5 Jim Carrey was working ________ a factory before he hit the big time.

a

b

c

d

e

## READING

**A PREDICT** Read the chatroom posts as quickly as you can and match each person with pictures (a–e).

1 Joel ___
2 Xavi ___
3 Margaret ___
4 Aisha ___
5 Claudio ___

**B READ FOR MAIN IDEA** Read the posts again and say how each person feels about their job. Write love (L) or hate (H) for each person.

1 Joel ___
2 Xavi ___
3 Margaret ___
4 Aisha ___
5 Claudio ___

**C SCAN** Read again and answer the questions below.

1 Which person says that his/her job is varied? ___
2 Which person sometimes meets famous people? ___
3 Which two people say their job can be physically uncomfortable? ___ ___
4 Which person says that he/she has a long vacation? ___
5 Which person mentions a colleague he/she doesn't like? ___
6 Which person says that people like talking to him/her? ___
7 Which person would like to work at a different time of the day? ___
8 Which person says that time passes very slowly? ___
9 Which person says that he/she enjoys seeing other people happy? ___
10 Which person feels that her job is not like work at all? ___
11 Which person gets money on top of his/her salary? ___
12 Which person says that people think the job is better than it really is? ___

**D REFLECT** Do you know anyone who really loves or really hates his or her job?

## Jobs We Love and Jobs We Hate

I drive a taxi in New York and I love every minute of it. I've done it for seven years and I've never been bored. Customers are either going to or coming back from somewhere interesting, and they enjoy a good chat. The taxi company doesn't pay me much, but I do well from the tips. I've picked up a few celebrities over the years, and they're generous. They sometimes tell me to keep the change from a $50 bill!

**Joel** – New York

Because of all the famous chefs on TV these days, people think it's a really interesting job. For most chefs, that's just not true. I've cooked since I finished college and I'm bored of it. I have to work when other people are enjoying themselves and I hardly ever see my kids. The kitchen's hot and people yell and bang pots and pans around. I work every evening on the weekend which isn't great for my social life.

**Xavi** – Barcelona

I really enjoy being an elementary school teacher. It's not the best paid job in the world but it's so satisfying. The look on the children's faces when I say they can play a game is worth a million dollars. It's great to have a lot of time off, too – almost six weeks in the summer.

**Margaret** – Oxford

I think I have the best job in the world. I'm a travel rep for a tour operator and I'm paid to have fun! I've done the job for three years and I've never done the same thing for more than three days. One day, I'm taking tourists on a bus tour and the next I'm playing volleyball on the beach. What a life!

**Aisha** – Bodrum

I guess you can say I work in construction, but I don't really build anything. I just do whatever I'm told to do. The foreman, my boss, is very rude and yells too much. I've spent this week knocking down walls with a huge electric drill … I was so tired and I'm still shaking! I look at my watch every ten minutes … days go on forever.

**Claudio** – Margate

### Glossary

**chat (v)** to talk in a friendly way
**drill (n)** a tool used for making a hole in something
**tip (n)** a small amount of money that you give to someone in addition to what you owe for service

## LISTENING

**A PREDICT** **Read the introduction to a radio show below. Check (✓) the points (1–8) that you think Jess or Kevin will mention.**

On this morning's show, we're talking about what makes a workplace a happy place. *New Profiles* is a company that is well known for keeping its employees happy. We wanted to know what this small company is doing right so we invited Jess and Kevin into the studio to tell us.

1 Being very well paid ☐
2 Making decisions ☐
3 Having a boss with a lot of experience ☐
4 Not having to work hard all the time ☐
5 Wearing casual clothes ☐
6 The workplace and its furniture ☐
7 Having a staff cafeteria ☐
8 Supporting the local community ☐

5.4 **B LISTEN FOR MAIN IDEA** **Listen and check your answers in Exercise A.**

5.4 **C LISTEN FOR DETAIL** **Listen again and choose the correct option in each sentence below.**

1 Jess designs the ***inside*** / ***outside*** of buildings.
2 Kevin works in sales ***alone*** / ***with other people***.
3 ***Jess decides*** / ***Somebody tells Jess*** what to do in her job.
4 Jess goes for a walk to ***stay in shape*** / ***get ideas***.
5 People working at *New Profiles* ***can*** / ***can't*** wear jeans to work.
6 Clients think *New Profiles* workers ***are dressed appropriately*** / ***should dress nicer***.
7 The inside of the *New Profiles* building is ***like*** / ***different from*** most other workplaces.
8 Jess and Kevin do work outside *New Profiles* ***for extra money*** / ***because they want to***.

5.5 **D LISTEN FOR INFERENCE** **Listen to two extracts from the recording and answer the questions below.**

1 Did Jess enjoy working at her previous job?

______________________

2 What did or didn't she like?

______________________

3 Did Kevin enjoy working at his previous job?

______________________

4 What did or didn't he like?

______________________

**E REFLECT** **Think about your answers to these questions.**

1 Do you think *New Profiles* would be an enjoyable place to work?
2 Do you think bosses should allow workers to decide when to work and when to take a break?
3 Have you heard about any companies like *New Profiles* in your country?

## FUNCTIONAL LANGUAGE

### Give information about your work experience in a job interview

5.6 **Match the interviewer's questions (1–7) below with the interviewee's answers (a–g). Then listen to check.**

1 Can you tell me something about yourself?
2 Who are you working for right now?
3 How long have you worked for them?
4 Do you have any particular responsibilities?
5 What are your main skills?
6 Are you good at working on a team?
7 Do you have any questions you'd like to ask?

a I'm with a company called *The Big Picture*. I'm in the research and development department.
b Yes, sharing ideas with colleagues is very important.
c Mmm, let me think. I'd like to know a little more about your flextime options.
d I've worked for them for six years.
e I communicate with clients confidently and I work well under pressure.
f I'm Greg and I'm 27. I like my current job, but I'm ready for a new challenge.
g I decide on the annual research budget.

## WRITING

**A** Read the ad from an English-speaking job website below. Answer the questions.

1 What is the purpose of an internship?

2 What are the advantages and disadvantages of doing an internship?

Looking to do something different this summer? Why not do an internship with us. We are the highest-rated tour guide company in the city.

We offer a week-long training course before you start taking tours out by yourself. So you'll soon learn how to bring the history of our amazing city to life.

This is not a paid job, but you can keep any tips and the experience is excellent.

You must be available to work weekends, be a people person and speak some English. You don't have to have any previous experience.

If you're interested, please send a cover email with your résumé to maria.ducas@citytourgroup.com.

**B** Read the beginning and ending of a cover letter below. Choose the correct phrase (1–4).

To: maria.ducas@citytourgroup.com
From: jorge.sanchez@madrid.es
Subject: Internship application

*[1]Dear Maria, / Dear Ms. Ducas,*

*[2]I would like to apply for the city tour guide internship. / I want to apply for the city tour guide internship.*

*[3]I hope to hear from you soon. / Get back to me soon!*

*[4]Love, / Sincerely yours,*

*Jorge Sanchez*

**C** Read the ad in Exercise A again. Check (✓) what an applicant needs to include in their cover email for the internship.

1 details about your experience and character ☐
2 why you want the internship ☐
3 what you know about the history of the city ☐
4 what qualifications you have ☐
5 a polite ending ☐
6 an informal greeting ☐
7 when you are available ☐
8 ask about the wage ☐

**D** Match the sentence halves.

1 Please find attached
2 The knowledge and skills I
3 I am fluent
4 Being an intern at your company

a developed there will be very helpful.
b in Italian and English.
c would be an exciting opportunity.
d a copy of my résumé.

## WRITING PRACTICE

**A** Plan your cover email to apply for the city tour guide internship.

- Use your ideas and the language from Writing Exercises B, C and D.
- Divide your writing into clear paragraphs.

**B** **WRITE** Write your cover email in 100–150 words.

## GRAMMAR
### Quantifiers *too* and *enough*

**A** Complete the second sentence so it has a similar meaning to the first sentence. You must use *too* + adjective, *too much*, *too many*, *enough* or *not enough*. Use three words.

1 The hospital needs one hundred doctors but it only has seventy-five.
The hospital doesn't ______________.

2 Ugh! This tea is too sugary.
Ugh! There's ______________ in this tea.

3 Jill doesn't need any more money. She can stop working.
Jill can stop working. She ______________.

4 There were a lot of children at my daughter's birthday party. It was so loud.
My daughter invited ______________ to her birthday party.

5 Susan only has 15 minutes to get to the airport. She's going to miss her flight.
Susan doesn't ______________ to get to the airport.

**B** Complete sentences a and b for each picture (1–3).

1

a The car isn't ______________.
b There are ______________ people for the car.

2

a The bag is ______________.
b The woman doesn't have ______________ to buy the handbag.

3

a The boy is ______________ to go on the ride.
b The boy isn't ______________ to go on the ride.

## VOCABULARY
### Minor illnesses

**A** Match the descriptions below to minor illnesses in the box.

a broken bone a cold a cough a headache a sore throat a temperature the flu a stomachache a sunburn a toothache

1 Graham's tired and all his muscles ache. He has a runny nose and a headache.
2 Jack fell and landed badly. He thought his ankle was twisted but it was more serious. His leg's in a cast.
3 Mary was sick last night. She ate too much at dinner.
4 Whenever Ray gets out of bed, he feels cold and shaky and his temperature is very high.
5 Louisa felt hot and unwell. The thermometer showed 37 °C and her mom said she had to stay at home.
6 Jane's sitting in the dark with the curtains closed. Light makes her feel worse. She's taken painkillers.
7 Tim thinks he has an infection of some kind. It hurts when he swallows.
8 Jasmine needs to see a dentist. She's been in pain for a few days and one side of her face is slightly swollen.
9 Adam fell asleep on the beach. His shoulders and back are very red and he has a headache.
10 Joanne's worried about her young son. She can hear him at night. She thinks he might have an infection, but it could also be the pollution in the big city they've just moved to.

**B** Match a verb (1–5) with a noun (a–e) to make common phrases.

| | |
|---|---|
| 1 go to | a sunscreen |
| 2 take | b bed / the hospital |
| 3 stay | c warm |
| 4 put on | d medicine / painkillers |
| 5 keep | e in bed / at home |

## PRONUNCIATION
### /ʌ/, /ɔː/, /uː/, /eɪ/ and /ɜː/

6.1 Circle the word which has a different vowel sound. Then listen to check.

1 flu / tooth / you / look
2 burn / come / sun / blood
3 ache / shake / head / pain
4 cough / sore / door / pour
5 hurt / short / learn / work

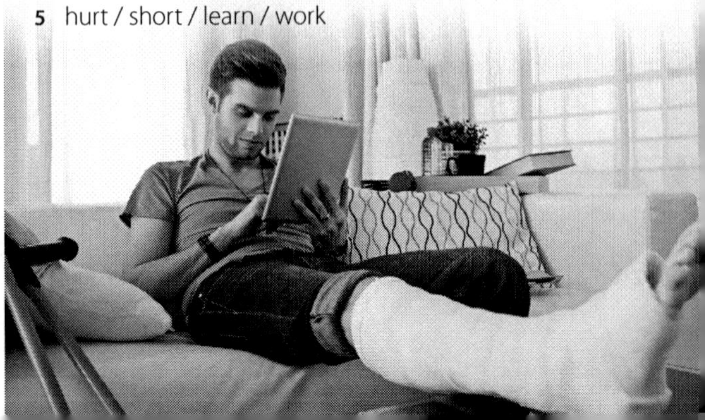

## VOCABULARY
### Exercise

**A** Cross out the activity that does not collocate with the verb.

1 do yoga / Nordic walking / jogging
2 go swimming / to the gym / a marathon
3 play a team sport / biking / tennis
4 run calories / a marathon / 10 km

**B** Complete the advertisement with the correct form of a verb in the box. Use some verbs more than once.

burn do go join stay
lose play run work out

## Heartbeat Fitness

Today, everyone wants to be healthy. People understand that [1]_______________ **in shape** is important and many of them want to [2]_______________ **weight**. Eating healthily is one consideration but [3]_______________ **regular exercise** is equally important. The problem is knowing what kind of exercise is best. Many people [4]_______________ **jogging** but find it boring and soon stop. Most people would love to [5]_______________ a **team sport**, but don't have the time to make a proper commitment. Here at Heartbeat, we know that [6]_______________ **a fitness club** is the perfect solution. Our activities and exercise options help you [7]_______________ **calories** while you have fun.

At Heartbeat you can [8]_______________ **in the gym**, [9]_______________ **racquetball** or [10]_______________ **yoga** and then go for a relaxing swim in our Olympic size pool. Our membership prices are very competitive – call now or visit our website. Who knows, maybe by next year, you will be planning to [11]_______________ **the New York City Marathon**!

## PRONUNCIATION
### /ŋ /, /n/ and /m/

6.2 Listen and write down the phrases.

1 _______________
2 _______________
3 _______________
4 _______________

## GRAMMAR
### *-ing* forms

**A** Choose whether the word in bold is an example of a gerund (G), adjective (A) or present participle (PP).

1 **Running** is my favorite form of exercise. G / A / PP
2 I'm **reading** a good book about yoga. G / A / PP
3 I don't like **working out** at the gym. G / A / PP
4 Recently, there has been a **growing** interest in Nordic walking. G / A / PP
5 My school's hockey team is **doing** really well this season. G / A / PP
6 People are exercising at home in **increasing** numbers. G / A / PP

**B** Complete the sentences below using an *-ing* form of a verb in the box.

disappoint excite live play relax run
wait watch work write

1 My mother's friend is _______________ a book about yoga.
2 Research shows that _______________ by the ocean is good for people's health.
3 There are too many people _______________ for taxis. Let's walk.
4 The gym is very popular with _______________ mothers. They usually go on their lunch break.
5 _______________ on a full stomach is not good for you.
6 My team's not _______________ well right now. They've had some _______________ results.
7 I'm going to go home and take a long, _______________ bath.
8 _______________ Roger Federer play tennis is one of the most _______________ sights in sports.

## GRAMMAR
### Present perfect with *just, already* and *yet*

**A** Read Lee's list of goals for the year. Write a sentence for each using the present perfect and *already* or *yet*.

*Diet*

1 *Stop drinking coffee.* X

2 *Start taking vitamin C tablets.* X

*Exercise*

3 *Find a personal fitness coach.* X

4 *Borrow Jim's exercise bike.* √

*Others*

5 *Quit smoking.* X

6 *Start going to bed at 10:00 pm.* √

1 ______.
2 ______.
3 ______.
4 ______.
5 ______.
6 ______.

**B** Rewrite each sentence using the present perfect with *just, already* or *yet*. Use three words for each. Contractions count as one word.

1 Juan was at the gym until ten minutes ago.
Juan ______ home from the gym.

2 I don't need to pack my suitcase. I did it this morning.
I ______ my suitcase. I did it this morning.

3 Is Katie still here?
______ Katie ______ the house ______?

4 Joe's fifteen but he still can't swim.
Joe's fifteen but he ______ to swim ______.

5 Jason and Lynn's plane arrived at Málaga Airport five minutes ago.
Jason and Lynn ______ in Málaga.

6 We saw this movie at the movie theater and again on Netflix.
We ______ this movie twice.

## PRONUNCIATION
### /s/ and /ʃ/

6.3 Listen and underline the word you hear. Then practice saying both words.

1 *sea / she*
2 *sell / shell*
3 *so / show*
4 *sake / shake*
5 *socks / shocks*
6 *Russ / rush*
7 *crust / crushed*
8 *myself / my shelf*

## VOCABULARY
### Food groups

Find fourteen more food items in the word search below.

| W | C | U | C | U | M | B | E | R | N | Z | Z |
|---|---|---|---|---|---|---|---|---|---|---|---|
| J | Q | D | R | L | O | B | S | T | E | R | K |
| J | O | B | H | S | B | T | O | M | A | T | O |
| C | M | M | V | K | N | A | O | A | T | S | O |
| Y | S | H | R | I | M | P | N | H | M | C | A |
| L | R | X | M | C | R | A | B | A | M | A | V |
| L | E | T | T | U | C | E | T | K | N | Q | O |
| U | R | V | I | F | K | P | W | U | Z | A | C |
| L | I | F | E | M | N | V | T | H | P | P | A |
| P | C | X | E | Z | X | U | I | B | E | Z | D |
| L | E | J | E | U | C | H | T | B | W | A | O |
| S | A | N | D | W | I | C | H | S | E | Y | T |

# Ten reasons to eat more chocolate

In great news for chocoholics, an increasing number of doctors now believe that chocolate is good for you. Here's why.

1 It's good for your heart. Chocolate contains fat, but not the fat we need to worry about. University of Cambridge researchers found that people who eat chocolate are 35% less at risk from heart disease.

2 It can help lower blood pressure. Chemicals in cocoa improve circulation.

3 It's good for your skin. Flavanols in chocolate are thought to protect you from sunburn.

4 It is a myth that chocolate gives you acne. No single food can cause bad skin; only a generally unhealthy diet can do that.

5 It is good for your bones. Chocolate contains calcium, which helps keep the skeleton strong.

6 It can help you lose weight. Eating a small amount of chocolate before a meal fills you and might mean that you then want to eat less.

7 You sleep better. Chocolate contains magnesium, which is very good for your body clock.

8 It's good for mothers and babies. One study shows that chocolate reduces stress in mothers-to-be and that the babies of these women smile more.

9 It improves brain power. Chemicals in chocolate improve thinking and reduce memory loss in older people.

10 It makes you feel happier. Chocolate contains the same chemical that your brain creates when you fall in love. Eating chocolate releases feel-good endorphins.

So, you can now eat chocolate without the guilt!

## READING

**A READ FOR MAIN IDEA** Read the title and the first line of the article. Is it claiming that chocolate is healthy or unhealthy?

**B SCAN** Read the article and underline the keywords or phrases that provide information about the ideas below.

1 It makes women who are expecting babies calmer.
2 Chocolate is romantic.
3 People who eat chocolate are more intelligent.
4 There is not so much danger of heart disease.
5 Blood moves better around the body.
6 Babies of mothers who eat chocolate are happier.
7 Older people don't forget things as much.
8 The body's natural system works better.
9 What people believe about chocolate and bad skin is untrue.
10 Chocolate is good for all the bones in the body.
11 People who eat chocolate might be thinner.
12 Chocolate might protect people if they lie in the sun.

**C REFLECT** Mark each reason (1–10) in the text using the following key.

K = I knew this before I read the article.

DK = I didn't know this and it's interesting. I think it's probably true.

DB = This is interesting but I don't believe this is true.

### Glossary

**at risk (phrase)** in danger / in a dangerous position or situation
**circulation (n)** the movement of something around a system
**memory loss (phrase)** inability to remember things
**mother-to-be (n)** a woman who will soon have a baby
**myth (n)** something that people wrongly believe to be true
**acne (n)** small mark on the face (or other parts of the body) caused by unhealthy lifestyle

## LISTENING

**A PREDICT** Check (✓) three countries below where you think people have a healthy lifestyle.

| | | | |
|---|---|---|---|
| France | ☐ | Brazil | ☐ |
| Greece | ☐ | Egypt | ☐ |
| Hong Kong | ☐ | Japan | ☐ |
| New Zealand | ☐ | Russia | ☐ |

6.4 **B LISTEN FOR MAIN IDEA** Listen to somebody talking about why people in three countries are especially healthy. Which countries from Exercise A do they mention?

1 ________ 2 ________ 3 ________

**Glossary**

**appreciate (v)** to recognize the good or special qualities of a person, place or thing
**encourage (v)** to suggest that someone does something that you believe would be good
**life expectancy (phrase)** the average age that people live to

6.4 **C LISTEN FOR DETAIL** Listen again. Match one of the three countries to each statement below.

1 Many people play sports. ________
2 Living to more than one hundred is not unusual. ________
3 Eating red meat isn't necessarily bad for you. ________
4 People go to different stores to buy food. ________
5 Fresh fish and seaweed are regularly on the menu. ________
6 People probably practice Tai Chi or Tae Kwando. ________
7 People like eating together in groups. ________
8 People don't spend time at home or working in unhealthy environments. ________
9 People probably don't have cars. ________
10 People don't eat too much as a single meal. ________

**D REFLECT** Think about your answers to these questions.

1 Do people in your country have a healthier or less healthy lifestyle than people in other countries?
2 Do younger people in your country have a more or less healthy lifestyle than older people?

## FUNCTIONAL LANGUAGE

### Talk about your symptoms at a pharmacy

6.5 **In each exchange below, delete one response that is not possible. Then listen to check.**

1 How are you feeling today?
  a I'm fine.
  b Not very well, actually.
  c I'll be fine.
2 What are your symptoms?
  a I have a sore throat and a headache.
  b I'm allergic to it.
  c I'm coughing a lot.
3 Does it hurt?
  a Yes, I'm sick today.
  b Yes, it's very painful.
  c Yes, it's really sore.
4 What do you suggest?
  a Take one of these every eight hours.
  b You have a bad cold.
  c You could try drinking hot lemon and honey.
5 What do you suggest?
  a I think you should rest.
  b You'll feel better soon.
  c Stay indoors and keep warm.
6 Are you allergic to anything?
  a Not that I know of.
  b I have hay fever at this time of the year.
  c I have a sore throat.
7 I usually get hay fever in the spring.
  a Yes, I know how you feel.
  b It's very common at this time of the year.
  c Are you allergic to anything?

a ___

They were expensive but I did feel a lot more active after only five classes. If you are only interested in improving your health, then they are **definitely worth the money**. But for people who like to have fun while exercising, **I don't recommend** these classes at all.

b ___

On a positive note, even though it was absolutely exhausting, I was **very happy** with the instructor – he kept everyone really motivated and introduced himself at the start of the class.

c ___

LIFE cycle: **slightly disappointed** ★★★☆☆

d ___

My friend **highly recommended** these spin classes as a fun and sociable way to get in shape. So, I thought why not give it a try.

e ___

However, the free gift of a pair of biking shorts was **poorly made**. I wore them once and they got a big hole in them. Also, the other people in the class weren't friendly. In fact, they were very competitive. This meant **the atmosphere wasn't great**.

## WRITING

**A** Think about the answers to these questions.

1. Why do people join gym classes?
2. What are the advantages of going to a class?
3. What are the disadvantages?

**B** Read the review. Put paragraphs (a–e) in the correct order.

**C** Decide whether the phrases in bold in the review are positive or negative. Write the phrases in the correct column in the table.

| Positive | Negative |
| --- | --- |
| | |

## WRITING PRACTICE

**A PREPARE** You are going to write a review of an exercise class which you have done or read about. Write notes about each of the points below.

- Choose an exercise class which you have done or read about.
- Decide what the positive points of taking the class were.
- Decide what the negative points of taking the class were.
- Think about your overall thoughts about the class and whether you would recommend it.

**B WRITE** Write your review in 100 words.

- Use your notes and ideas from Exercise A.
- Divide your writing into clear paragraphs.

# Irregular Verbs

| Base form | Past simple | Past participle |
| --- | --- | --- |
| be | was/were | been |
| become | became | become |
| begin | began | begun |
| break | broke | broken |
| bring | brought | brought |
| build | built | built |
| buy | bought | bought |
| can | could | (been able to) |
| catch | caught | caught |
| choose | chose | chosen |
| come | came | come |
| cost | cost | cost |
| cut | cut | cut |
| do | did | done |
| drink | drank | drunk |
| eat | ate | eaten |
| fall | fell | fallen |
| feel | felt | felt |
| find | found | found |
| forget | forgot | forgotten |
| get | got | got |
| give | gave | given |
| go | went | gone/been |
| grow | grew | grown |
| have | had | had |
| hear | heard | heard |
| hit | hit | hit |
| hold | held | held |
| hurt | hurt | hurt |
| keep | kept | kept |
| know | knew | known |
| leave | left | left |
| lend | lent | lent |

| Base form | Past simple | Past participle |
| --- | --- | --- |
| let | let | let |
| lose | lost | lost |
| make | made | made |
| mean | meant | meant |
| meet | met | met |
| must | had to | (had to) |
| pay | paid | paid |
| put | put | put |
| read | read | read |
| ride | rode | ridden |
| run | ran | run |
| say | said | said |
| see | saw | seen |
| sell | sold | sold |
| set | set | set |
| shut | shut | shut |
| sing | sang | sung |
| sit | sat | sat |
| sleep | slept | slept |
| speak | spoke | spoken |
| spell | spelled | spelled |
| spend | spent | spent |
| stand | stood | stood |
| steal | stole | stolen |
| take | took | taken |
| teach | taught | taught |
| tell | told | told |
| think | thought | thought |
| throw | threw | thrown |
| understand | understood | understood |
| wear | wore | worn |
| win | won | won |
| write | wrote | written |

| PHONETIC SYMBOLS | | | | | | | | | | | | | | |
| --- | --- | --- | --- | --- | --- | --- | --- | --- | --- | --- | --- | --- | --- | --- |
| Single vowels | | | Diphthongs | | | Consonants | | | | | | | | |
| /ɪ/ | f**i**sh | /fɪʃ/ | /ɪə/ | **ear** | /ɪə/ | /p/ | **p**en | /pen/ | /s/ | **s**nake | /sneɪk/ |
| /iː/ | b**ea**n | /biːn/ | /eɪ/ | f**a**ce | /feɪs/ | /b/ | **b**ag | /bæg/ | /z/ | **z**oo | /zuː/ |
| /ʊ/ | f**oo**t | /fʊt/ | /ʊə/ | t**ou**rist | /'tʊərɪst/ | /t/ | **t**ea | /tiː/ | /ʃ/ | **sh**op | /ʃɒp/ |
| /uː/ | sh**oe** | /ʃuː/ | /ɔɪ/ | b**oy** | /bɔɪ/ | /d/ | **d**og | /dɒg/ | /ʒ/ | televi**si**on | /'telɪvɪʒən/ |
| /e/ | **e**gg | /eg/ | /əʊ/ | n**o**se | /nəʊz/ | /ʧ/ | **ch**ip | /ʧɪp/ | /m/ | **m**ap | /mæp/ |
| /ə/ | moth**er** | /'mʌðə/ | /ju/ | **u**se | /juz/ | /ʤ/ | **j**azz | /ʤæz/ | /n/ | **n**ame | /neɪm/ |
| /ɜː/ | w**or**d | /wɜːd/ | /aɪ/ | **eye** | /aɪ/ | /k/ | **c**ake | /keɪk/ | /ŋ/ | ri**ng** | /rɪŋ/ |
| /ɔː/ | t**a**lk | /tɔːk/ | /aʊ/ | m**ou**th | /maʊθ/ | /g/ | **g**irl | /gɜːl/ | /h/ | **h**ouse | /haʊs/ |
| /æ/ | b**a**ck | /bæk/ | | | | /f/ | **f**ilm | /fɪlm/ | /l/ | **l**eg | /leg/ |
| /ʌ/ | b**u**s | /bʌs/ | | | | /v/ | **v**erb | /vɜːb/ | /r/ | **r**oad | /rəʊd/ |
| /ɑː/ | **ar**m | /ɑːm/ | | | | /θ/ | **th**ing | /θɪŋ/ | /w/ | **w**ant | /wɒnt/ |
| /ɒ/ | t**o**p | /tɒp/ | | | | /ð/ | **th**ese | /ðiːz/ | /j/ | **y**es | /jes/ |

## UNIT 1

### 1.4 Lesson 1.5, Listening, Exercise B

**T = Teacher Ja = Javier**
**Am = Amelie Ah = Ahmed**
**Ju = Junko Ac = Achara**

T: Good morning students. I'd like to know about greetings in your countries. So, Javier, tell us about greetings in Spain. I know how to say *hola* but not much more.

Ja: Well yes, we say *hola* but also when we meet somebody for the first time and they introduce themselves, we say *encantado*. That's like saying *pleased to meet you*.

T: And do people shake hands or kiss on the cheek?

Ja: Two men usually shake hands, but they hug if they are good friends. If people meet for the first time, it depends. Men shake hands, while women usually place a kiss on each cheek.

T: And Amelie, I guess that's similar in Belgium?

Am: Mm, very similar but we're a little more formal. Female friends kiss on each cheek … sometimes three times. Male friends tend to shake hands. When meeting for the first time, most people shake hands. We usually say *bonjour* and that simply means *good day*. In the evening, we say *bonsoir*.

T: Ahmed, how do people greet each other in Oman?

Ah: Well, there's a traditional greeting. Male friends say hello by touching noses. It shows they're very close friends. People do this in other parts of the Middle East. In more formal situations, men shake hands, but it must be the right hand, of course. A man doesn't usually shake a woman's hand. There are many ways to greet somebody by speaking, but *marhaba* is easy. It just means *hello*.

T: Junko, can you tell us about greetings in Japan?

Ju: Well, you probably know that people say *konnichiwa* to say *hello* or *good day*. People bow when they meet. They bow in different ways depending on the relationship with the other person.

T: Achara, do people bow when they greet people in Thailand?

Ac: Yes, but we only bow our head a little. We press the palms of our hands together and bow our head forward. Not everyone always does this, of course. To say *hello* we say *sawasdee*. Men say *sawasdee khrap* and women say *sawasdee kha*. It's a little difficult to explain properly.

T: Well, that was fascinating. Now we're going to …

### 1.5 Lesson 1.5, Functional Language

**D = Daniel L = Liz**

D: Hi, Liz. What a nice surprise. It's great to see you.

L: You, too … long time no see! How's it going?

D: I'm good. Things are going well. How about you … what's new?

L: Well, I just got back from traveling in Asia. It was amazing.

**G = Gavin C = Claire**

G: Let me introduce myself. I'm Gavin.

C: Hi Gavin, I'm Claire. Nice to meet you. What do you do?

G: I'm working in a bookstore for now.

C: Do you enjoy it?

G: Well, it's not my dream job but it pays the rent.

**S = Simon T = Tom**

S: Would you like another drink?

T: Sorry, I have to go now.

S: Really, why so early?

T: I have my driving test tomorrow … at 8:30!

S: Oh OK. Good luck!

## UNIT 2

### 2.4 Lesson 2.5, Listening, Exercise A

**P = Presenter J = Julia**

P: Now, I'm joined in the studio by local politician Julia Day. She's going to tell us about a project called *Houseshare*. The goal of the project is to help both old people who are lonely and find it difficult to care for themselves and young people who need somewhere to live.

### 2.5 Lesson 2.5, Listening, Exercise C

**P = Presenter J = Julia**

P: Now, I'm joined in the studio by local politician Julia Day. She's going to tell us about a project called *Houseshare*. The goal of the project is to help both old people who are lonely and find it difficult to care for themselves and young people who need somewhere to live.

J: Good morning.

P: Good morning, Julia. Now, what makes *Houseshare* special?

J: Well, we have two things happening in society that affect property. One is that we have an aging population – more people are living longer and so we have more older people. The other is that property prices are going up and up and young people can't find anywhere to live. There just aren't enough low-cost accommodations. *Houseshare* is designed to help both of these types of people with one solution.

P: Hmm … that sounds interesting. And, tell us what you mean exactly.

J: Well, a lot of older people have a spare room in their house. Maybe they're living alone because their husband or wife died, or their children have left home. They could be lonely or find it difficult to look after the house. *Houseshare* helps people stay in the place they call home. At the same time, for young people it's becoming impossible to find low-cost accommodations. They have no chance of buying a home of their own and rent is so expensive.

P: So, older people give a room in their house to a young person?

J: That's right. In return, the younger person helps around the house and is a companion for the older person.

P: What sort of help does the young person give?

J: Well, usually, it's cleaning and cooking. Frequently, the older person needs someone to go shopping or walk their dog. The young person usually has a car and can drive the older person to places.

P: I see. How many hours is the young person expected to help? I mean, if they spend all day caring for the old person, they can't go to work or see their own friends.

J: The idea is that the young person spends ten hours a week helping and being a companion. He or she pays rent to the older homeowner, but it's reduced. The accommodation is low-cost, but it's not free.

P: Hmm. Tell us something about safety. I mean, is it safe for an older person to invite a young person to live in their house?

J: The interviews for *Houseshare* are very strict and the young person is asked a lot of questions. They can only move into a house if the organization is totally sure he or she is safe.

P: So, is *Houseshare* only operating in the US?

J: No, absolutely not. It's successful all over the world. There are projects across Europe and in Australia. It's growing all the time.

### 2.6 Lesson 2.5, Functional language

1 What should I do? Should I move to New York?

g I'm not sure it's a good idea to leave home so soon.

2 Why don't I take care of the kids for you?

d Well, only if you're sure. They're no trouble.

3 You could tell Stuart to start exercising.

f Seriously? Do you think he ever listens to me?

4 Why don't you ask your parents to help?

a No, I can't rely on them all the time.

5 I think you should try eating at the new restaurant.

h Thanks, I'll try it. I really like Thai food.

6 How about staying with Jill and Martin?

b Yeah, good idea. They have a spare room.

7 There's no cream. What do you suggest?

c How about using milk instead?

8 Let me take you to the station.

e Well, if you're going that way. Thanks.

## UNIT 3

### 3.4 Lesson 3.5, Listening, Exercise B

**M = Man YM = Young male**
**YF = Young female**

YM: Excuse me. Can you help us? We need to find the *Europa Guest House*. Do you know it?

M: The *Europa*? Yes, I do. It's on Vicarage Road, isn't it?

YF: Yes, that's right.

M: It's fairly easy. Go straight down this road in front of us … Station Road … for about seven or eight minutes. Don't turn off. You'll go past a big hotel, the *Hilton*, and then, after another couple of minutes, you'll come to a big fountain in the middle of the road.

YM: A fountain … you mean with water in it?

M: Yes, it's a roundabout with roads off it. Turn right there and walk up the hill. Take the third turn on the left – there's a restaurant on the corner called *Duke's*. The *Europa* is on the right about a hundred meters up the road.

YF: Thank you very much.

3.5 **Lesson 3.5, Listening, Exercise C**
**M = Man YM = Young male**
**YF = Young female**

YF: Thank you very much. Can you tell us how long the walk will take?

M: From here it'll take about fifteen minutes if you're walking with those suitcases.

YF: Our bags are very heavy. Is there a bus that goes that way?

M: You can get a bus from right here. The bus stop's across the road and you want the number 19. To tell you the truth, though, it'll probably take longer by bus than walking … at least twenty minutes. The traffic's really bad on Station Road.

YM: Do you know how much the bus trip is?

M: Yes, every trip in the town center costs one dollar and fifty cents.

YM: So, that'll be three dollars for the two of us.

M: Yes, and since you're only going a few stops, it's a little expensive. You can jump in a taxi and get there much quicker.

YF: And how much is the taxi?

M: It'll be about four dollars … not much more than the bus for two people.

YF: What do you think we should do?

YM: Let's just get a taxi.

3.6 **Lesson 3.5, Functional Language, Exercise A**

1 A: That bag looks heavy. Let me help you with it.
B: No, don't worry, I can manage.

2 A: Here, don't forget your cell phone.
B: Oh, thanks. I'd be lost without it.

3 A: Which way's platform 3?
B: I'm going that way too. Follow me.

4 A: Do I have to change trains on this trip?
B: No, this one's direct.

5 A: Is that the train I want on platform 2?
B: Yes, hurry up. It leaves in two minutes. You don't want to miss it.

6 A: What time does the train arrive in the city?
B: At 2:35.

# UNIT 4

4.4 **Lesson 4.5, Listening, Exercise B**

Speaker 1

The biggest change will be the aging population. By 2050, the number of people over 65 will be three times what it is now. In some places, the largest age group in society will be the over 65s and the average age of the population will be 50. That will mean a huge amount of money spent on healthcare. Imagine if people retire at 60 or 65 and then live for another 40 years. Who will pay for it?

Speaker 2

An aging population might have a big impact on education, especially the way students experience further education. Over the next 20 years, there will gradually be fewer 18-to-23-year-olds. Right now, there aren't many mature students but that will certainly change. If the population grows older, the typical student in further education might be 35 or 40. College life will be much more adult.

Speaker 3

I'm interested in the buildings of the future. By 2050, most people will be living in cities, and many will live in huge sustainable buildings. People in these buildings will produce their own food. They'll grow fruits and vegetables and have floors where people can raise farm animals and fish. The buildings will be like vertical towns with shopping malls, banks, restaurants and movie theaters. Some people will leave the buildings to go to work or school, but the biggest buildings might have offices and schools within. Some people will only leave to visit friends or go on vacation.

Speaker 4

We know that in the future many more people will live in cities, but it's crazy to say that they'll all live in amazing modern buildings. The truth is that millions will live in extreme poverty in shanty towns – that means areas with houses that aren't built properly and usually don't have electricity or water. These places exist now, of course, but they'll grow far bigger. Some will be home to a million people – they'll be cities inside cities. The police will find them impossible to control.

Speaker 5

I'll be interested to see how the internet changes human interaction. In conventional face-to-face interaction, there are rules of behavior that everyone understands. Online, people are anonymous – they don't always use their name or photo, so they can say what they like. They are usually ruder and more aggressive. Maybe we'll get bored of using the internet soon, but if we continue the way we are, we'll forget how to use normal language.

4.5 **Lesson 4.5, Functional Language**
**E = Emily M = Maria G = Greg**
**D = Dave**

1 E: Do you want to eat out this evening?
M: Yeah, I'd love to. Could we try that new Korean place by the bus station?
E: Yes, sounds great.
M: Oh, wait a minute. I just remembered that my sister's coming over. She wants to talk about Mom and Dad's anniversary.
E: Well, that's OK. You can talk about it and then we'll go out for dinner.

2 G: Hi Dave, it's me … Greg. Are you free on Saturday night?
D: I'm not sure. I'll just check my calendar. Um. Yes, I'm free. Did you want to meet for a drink or something?
G: Actually, I'm hoping you could babysit. Emma and I are going to the theater.
D: Yeah, OK then. What time?
G: Could you be here at 7:30?
D: I'm so sorry – I can't do that time because I'll be at my Spanish class until 8:00. How about 8:15?
G: Great, 8:15 it is.

# UNIT 5

5.4 **Lesson 5.5, Listening, Exercise B**
**P = Presenter J = Jess K = Kevin**

P: On this morning's show, we're talking about what makes a workplace a happy place. *New Profiles* is a company that is well known for keeping its employees happy. We wanted to know what this small company is doing right, so we invited Jess and Kevin into the studio to tell us. Good morning.

JK: Good morning.

P: First, tell us what jobs you do at *New Profiles*.

J: Well, I'm a designer. I design interiors … for kitchens or bathrooms.

K: And I work in sales … on a team of six.

P: And are you both happy at work?

J: Definitely. I've been at *New Profiles* for three years and I love it.

K: I agree. It's very relaxed and people like each other.

P: So, what's the secret?

J: For me it's about making decisions on my own. I mean, nobody tells me what to do and nobody watches what I'm doing. Where I worked before, my boss was always looking over my shoulder to see if I was busy.

P: So, are you usually busy?

J: Most of the day, yes … but there are times when I don't feel creative. At *New Profiles*, nobody expects me to sit and stare at my computer. I can go out for a walk or play a computer game. An idea will come to me. What's important is the final design … not how many hours I've worked.

K: Yes, and for me wearing what I like to work is important. At *New Profiles*, people dress in jeans and even shorts when it's hot. Our clients understand our philosophy … they don't care how we dress. At my last job, I had to wear a suit all day and it was really uncomfortable.

P: Tell me about the physical environment. I mean, is it a pleasant building to work in?

J: It's very stylish and very different from where most people work. The walls are painted different colors and the furniture's very colorful. All the computer chairs are different colors and there is a bright pink couch.

K: Yeah, it all looks really cool, and Jess forgot to mention the pool table in the middle of the staff area.

J: *New Profiles* likes to give something back, too. I mean, one morning a month, each of us does something to help the local community. I go and help at a shelter for homeless people and Kevin teaches kids computer skills at an elementary school. It's very satisfying.

P: Well, it sounds like a nice place to work. You're both very lucky.

**Lesson 5.5, Listening, Exercise D**

5.5 **J = Jess K = Kevin**

1 J: I mean, nobody tells me what to do and nobody watches what I'm doing. Where I worked before, my boss was always looking over my shoulder to check if I was busy.

2 K: At my last job, I had to wear a suit all day and it was really uncomfortable.

**Lesson 5.5, Functional Language**

5.6 **I = Interviewer G = Greg**

1 I: Can you tell me something about yourself?

G: I'm Greg and I'm 27. I like my current job, but I'm ready for a new challenge.

2 I: Who are you working for right now?

G: I'm with a company called *The Big Picture*. I'm in the research and development department.

3 I: How long have you worked for them?

G: I've worked for them for six years.

4 I: Do you have any particular responsibilities?

G: I decide on the annual research budget.

5 I: What are your main skills?

G: I communicate with clients confidently and I work well under pressure.

6 I: Are you good at working on a team?

G: Yes, sharing ideas with colleagues is very important.

7 I: Do you have any questions you'd like to ask?

G: Mmm, let me think. I'd like to know a little more about your flextime options.

# UNIT 6

**Lesson 6.5, Listening, Exercise B**

6.4 **P = Presenter**
**PM = Professor Glynis Mann**

P: On *Healthy Bodies* this morning, we've been talking about lifestyles. Now, we're going to talk to Professor Glynis Mann, who studies health and culture in various parts of the world. She's going to tell us why people in some countries are healthier and live longer. Good morning, Professor.

PM: Good morning.

P: So, is health and fitness more about diet or more about exercise and keeping active?

PM: It's definitely both. I think most people know that Japan has the highest life expectancy … people expect to live longer. In Japan average life expectancy is 86 for women and 79 for men and it's improving all the time. People enjoy a healthy diet with lots of fresh fish and vegetables. Seaweed is especially good for you. At the same time, the government encourages people to join fitness centers, practice martial arts or follow exercise programs at home. On one small Japanese island, Okinawa, people are especially healthy. There are more people over a hundred years old than anywhere else on Earth.

P: And I heard that people in Japan eat a number of small meals rather than one or two big meals in a day.

PM: Yes, that's right. Eat until you're not hungry, they say. In the West, we usually eat big meals and keep eating even when we're already full!

P: I've heard that New Zealand is another place where people have healthy lifestyles.

PM: Yes, now that might be because of the small population. New Zealand is a large country but only four and a half million people live there. There isn't a lot of industry and pollution is just not a problem. Many people have outdoor jobs, and, in their free time, people enjoy healthy outdoor activities, like camping and rock climbing. Rugby is very popular. People in New Zealand eat a lot of red meat, but it's free range meat. The animals are healthy and the meat isn't full of chemicals. Men especially have less heart disease than men in other countries.

P: Now, I'm very interested in why people in Greece are so healthy. It's a place I've visited and I love it.

PM: Oh yes, me too. Again, it has a small population and many people live in small towns. They walk a lot … maybe five kilometers a day. People eat a very healthy range of natural products … fresh vegetables and meat from local farms. Everything is cooked in the best olive oil so there's very little fat in the diet. People don't buy all their food in grocery stores … they visit the butcher, the bakery and fruit and vegetable stands. People see eating as a social activity. They enjoy meals with family and friends whenever possible and they take a long time to appreciate their food.

P: Well, thank you so much, Professor. I think I'm going to have to think more about my own …

**Lesson 6.5, Functional language**

6.5
1 A: How are you feeling today?

B: I'm fine.

A: How are you feeling today?

B: Not very well, actually.

2 A: What are your symptoms?

B: I have a sore throat and a headache.

A: What are your symptoms?

B: I'm coughing a lot.

3 A: Does it hurt?

B: Yes, it's very painful.

A: Does it hurt?

B: Yes, it's really sore.

4 A: What do you suggest?

B: Take one of these every eight hours.

A: What do you suggest?

B: You could try drinking hot lemon and honey.

5 A: What do you suggest?

B: I think you should rest.

A: What do you suggest?

B: Stay indoors and keep warm.

6 A: Are you allergic to anything?

B: Not that I know of.

A: Are you allergic to anything?

B: I get hay fever at this time of the year.

7 A: I usually get hay fever in the spring.

B: Yes, I know how you feel.

A: I usually get hay fever in the spring.

B: It's very common at this time of the year.

# Answer key

## 1.1 Breaking the ice

### GRAMMAR

**A**

**1** Are you enjoying
**2** how do you know
**3** Did you study
**4** Have you been
**5** Were you

**B**

**1** do, c **2** are, f **3** do, a **4** Did, e **5** were, b **6** Have, d

### VOCABULARY

**A**

**1** children
**2** parents
**3** relatives
**4** grandparents
**5** Friends
**6** Colleagues
**7** Strangers
**8** Teachers, students

**B**

**1** colleagues **2** friends **3** strangers **4** relatives
**5** grandparents

### PRONUNCIATION

**1** S **2** D **3** S **4** D **5** S **6** S **7** D **8** S

## 1.2 Blogs and bloggers

### VOCABULARY

**A**

**1** people person
**2** foodie
**3** mother of four
**4** sports fan
**5** gamer
**6** traveler
**7** blogger

**B**

**1** a **2** b **3** a **4** b

### PRONUNCIATION

**1** culture **2** beauty **3** regularly

### GRAMMAR

**A**

**1** d **2** c **3** e **4** b **5** a

**B**

**1** Julie never checks personal emails at work.
**2** I call my friend twice a day.
**3** You can always buy pizza at the restaurant.
**4** He hardly ever walks to school.
**5** They visit their grandparents three times a year.
**6** Emma is rarely late for her class.

## 1.3 Personality

### GRAMMAR

**A**

**1** anywhere **2** everything **3** something **4** Nowhere
**5** everyone **6** somewhere **7** Nobody **8** somebody's

**B**

**1** ~~somebody~~ anybody / anyone **2** ~~are~~ is
**3** ~~everything~~ anything / something **4** ~~like~~ likes
**5** ~~anybody's~~ somebody's / someone's
**6** ~~anything~~ nothing / isn't anything

### PRONUNCIATION

re<u>spon</u>sible <u>beau</u>tiful hard-<u>working</u> <u>con</u>fident
<u>sen</u>sible inde<u>pen</u>dent <u>so</u>ciable cre<u>a</u>tive <u>cur</u>ious
disa<u>ppoin</u>ted

### VOCABULARY

**A**

**Across:** **3** creative **7** well organized **8** shy
**9** independent
**Down:** **1** sociable **2** hard-working **4** curious **5** lazy
**6** sensible

**B**

**1** with **2** at **3** in **4** in **5** in **6** for

## 1.4 Reading

### READING

**A**

**1** b
**2 a** F **b** T **c** T

**C**

**1** quizzer **2** informer **3** changeling **4** watcher **5** novice
**6** troll **7** fanatic **8** egoist

## 1.5 Listening; Functional Language

### LISTENING

**A**

**1** d
**2** c
**3** b
**4** a

**B**

**1** Spain **2** Pleased **3** hug **4** Belgium **5** day **6** three
**7** close **8** right **9** Japan **10** relationship **11** men
**12** women

### FUNCTIONAL LANGUAGE

**1** d, c, a, b
**2** c, b, e, a, d
**3** d, a, e, b, c

## 1.6 Write information about yourself

### WRITING

**A**
your age, your job, your likes / dislikes, what type of person you are

**B**
yes

**C**
~~add~~ ad (S); ~~interested with~~ interested in (V); ~~interested in watch~~ interested in watching (G); ~~dog owner~~ dog lover (V); ~~chating~~ chatting (S); ~~anything~~ something (V)

### WRITING PRACTICE

**B**
**Model answer**
Hi Jessica,
I'm writing about your ad for a new roommate. My name's Veronica and I'm studying to be a vet. I am a real animal lover! I enjoy watching movies and going to the gym, when I'm not studying. I like eating healthy food but I don't like cooking because I'm not very good at it.
I look forward to hearing from you.
Best wishes,
Elizabeth

## 2.1 Love where you live

### GRAMMAR

**A**
1 some extremely tall buildings
2 was fairly good
3 are really friendly
4 are so excited
5 We almost won
6 has changed completely / completely changed

**B**
1 it's really complicated
2 it was really easy
3 the center has completely changed / changed completely
4 I've almost finished the first chapter
5 the population is growing quickly
6 he's a very tall boy now

### VOCABULARY

**A**
1 ~~music~~ 2 ~~food~~ 3 ~~trees~~
4 ~~river~~ 5 ~~art~~ 6 ~~sky~~

**B**
1 dirty 2 peaceful 3 inconvenient 4 lively

### PRONUNCIATION
complete, direct, extreme

## 2.2 The boomerang generation

### VOCABULARY

**A**
1 about 2 with 3 on 4 with 5 for

**B**
1 talk with / to
2 talk about
3 argue with
4 looking for
5 rely on

### PRONUNCIATION
1 sp, sl 2 st, sn 3 sw, sm 4 sl, st 5 st, sw 6 sm, sc
7 sn, sk 8 sn, st

### GRAMMAR

**A**
1 works 2 is playing 3 picks up 4 takes 5 isn't working
6 's / is having 7 study 8 are reading

**B**
1 're living 2 'm looking for 3 don't want 4 know
5 don't think 6 Does, own 7 are increasing 8 understand

## 2.3 Time flies

### GRAMMAR

**A**
1 carried
2 came
3 gave
4 had
5 liked
6 made
7 played
8 planned
9 took
10 stopped

**B**
1 hoped
2 didn't want
3 came
4 were
5 bought
6 wasn't
7 put
8 noticed
9 arrived
10 didn't worry
11 got
12 couldn't

### PRONUNCIATION
1 S 2 D 3 S 4 S
5 S 6 D 7 D 8 S

### VOCABULARY
1 get a job 2 retired 3 get married 4 have children
5 fell in love 6 go to college 7 leave home
8 get my own place 9 left school 10 learn to swim

## 2.4 Reading

### READING

**A**
b

**B**
**1** a **2** c **3** d **4** b

**C**
**1** F They might complain about having no entertainment or recreational facilities.
**2** F Many in this age group cannot live where they would ideally like to.
**3** T
**4** F Some people in this age group enjoy city life.
**5** F People over 55 have different priorities.
**6** T

## 2.5 Listening; Functional Language

### LISTENING

**B**
**1** older people and young people
**2** It costs a lot to buy or rent property.
**3** They don't have family. / They are lonely. / They need help around their house. / They find it difficult to care for themselves.

**C**
**1** O **2** Y **3** O **4** O **5** Y **6** Y

### FUNCTIONAL LANGUAGE
**1** g **2** d **3** f **4** a **5** h **6** b **7** c **8** e

## 2.6 Write an email of complaint

### WRITING

**A**
**1** c **2** b **3** a

**B**
2, 4, 5, 1, 3

**C**
**1** and **2** or **3** but **4** because **5** so

**D**
**a** 1 **b** 3 **c** 2 **d** 5 **e** 4

### WRITING PRACTICE

**B**
**Model answer**
Dear Sir/Madam,
I am writing to complain about a tent I bought in one of your stores recently.
I took my family camping last weekend. We set up the tent and went to sleep. Then I woke up in the middle of the night to rain dripping onto the sleeping bag from a small hole in the roof.
When I took the tent back to the store, I was told I could exchange the tent for another one. However, I would prefer to have my money back because we will not be going camping again this year.
Please issue me a refund as soon as possible.
Sincerely yours, Vincenzo

## 3.1 The four-year journey

### GRAMMAR

**A**
**1** Correct
**2** Some of
**3** Correct
**4** Correct
**5** ~~No~~ None
**6** most of my
**7** ~~no~~ none
**8** All of them

### PRONUNCIATION
**1** pack your bag
**2** a very big plane
**3** the visa is in your passport
**4** visit the port
**5** the best pizza in Venice
**6** a very big park in Barcelona

### VOCABULARY

**A**
**1** car
**2** plane
**3** ferry
**4** taxi
**5** minivan
**6** helicopter
**7** train
**8** bus
**9** bus
**10** motorcycle

**B**
**1** travel **2** get **3** take a **4** by **5** flew

## 3.2 Lost at sea

### GRAMMAR

**A**
**1** Did they enjoy
**2** was sleeping
**3** didn't take
**4** Were you living
**5** started

**B**
**1** was traveling **2** were walking **3** yelled
**4** didn't speak **5** ran **6** saw **7** was beating **8** picked
**9** moved

**C**
**1** while, was waiting **2** when, lost **3** while, was driving
**4** when, said **5** While, were talking

### PRONUNCIATION
**1** We were playing chess.
**2** Is she going?
**3** What were they doing?
**4** Was he living in Brooklyn?
**5** Where are you going?

### VOCABULARY

**A**

**1** dishonest **2** incorrect **3** impossible **4** unusual
**5** impatient **6** unlucky **7** unhealthy

**B**

**1** unhappy, c **2** impolite, a **3** disorganized, f
**4** inaccurate, b **5** unkind, d **6** unlikely, e **7** unfriendly, g

## 3.3 Too good to be true

### GRAMMAR

**A**

~~remember packing~~ remember to pack; ~~need worrying~~ need to worry; ~~doesn't mind to drive~~ doesn't mind driving; ~~need leaving~~ need to leave; ~~spend time to shop~~ spend time shopping; ~~manage getting~~ manage to get; ~~finish to pack~~ finish packing

**B**

**1** going out with Tim and Suzy **2** to rent a car **3** reading it
**4** playing tennis after our friend went home **5** to give me the money

### VOCABULARY

**A**

**1** f **2** e **3** a **4** b **5** c **6** i **7** d **8** j **9** h **10** g

**B**

**Across:** **2** spa **3** air conditioner **6** dorm
**Down:** **1** balcony **4** chalet **5** campsite
**7** front desk **8** gym

### PRONUNCIATION

**1** choose **2** genuine **3** chalet **4** picture **5** change

## 3.4 Reading

### READING

**A**

**a** 3 **b** 4 **c** 2 **d** 6 **e** 1 **f** 5

**B**

**1** F **2** I **3** I **4** F **5** F **6** I

**C**

**1** F Passengers don't usually need to change trains on trips between two big cities.
**2** T
**3** F Paula's going on a boat tomorrow.
**4** F Paula is staying in a large hotel.
**5** F The blog writer doesn't like package vacations.
**6** F The blog writer thinks people who go on package vacations aren't interested in culture.
**7** T
**8** T
**9** F The check-in manager at the airport didn't help the traveler.
**10** T

## 3.5 Listening; Functional Language

### LISTENING

**B**

d

**C**

**1** 15 minutes **2** 19 **3** 20 minutes **4** $1.50 **5** $4

**D**

**1** a **2** b **3** b **4** a **5** b

### FUNCTIONAL LANGUAGE

**A**

**1** help, worry
**2** forget
**3** follow
**4** change
**5** miss
**6** arrive

**B**

**1** At **2** in **3** at **4** to **5** to / from **6** in **7** from **8** at
**9** ahead / to

## 3.6 Write an email about a travel experience

### WRITING

**A**

**1** sunburn, a **2** food poisoning, c **3** insect bite, b
**4** delayed flight, d

**B**

sunburn and food poisoning

**C**

**1** First **2** The next day **3** hours **4** After **5** then

### WRITING PRACTICE

**B**

**Model answer**

Hi Andrew,
How are you? I just got back from vacation in Italy. It was good, but a few things went wrong.
First, my flight was delayed by six hours. When I finally landed in Rome, the taxi driver took me to the wrong hotel. A few hours later, I managed to find the right one and checked in.
The weather was nice the next day, so I went sightseeing. I also ate some delicious food – pasta, pizza and ice cream.
The day after was even hotter though and I got sunburned as I walked around the Colosseum. It was really painful.
I hope I'm not as unlucky on my next vacation.
Talk to you soon!
Sam

## 4.1 What's the plan?

### VOCABULARY

**A**

**1** hanging out with
**2** (to) go to
**3** to play

4 went for
5 went to
6 went for

B
1 wife for a
2 went to an amazing
3 hang out with their
4 going out for coffee
5 see a movie
6 to play in the park
7 been for/on a long
8 play cards

### GRAMMAR

A
1 are going to give up
2 are going to travel
3 is going to buy
4 is going to paint
5 are going to give
6 aren't going to move

B
1 Yes, they are. 2 Yes, they are. 3 No, he isn't. / No, he's not.
4 Yes, she is. 5 No, they aren't. / No, they're not.
6 Yes, they are.

C
**Suggested answers**
1 Are you doing 2 I'm taking 3 We're meeting
4 I'm going to take 5 They're flying 6 I'm going to watch

### PRONUNCIATION
1 Are you gonna come with us?
2 We're gonna buy a car.
3 She's gonna see a movie.

## 4.2 The future of free time
### GRAMMAR

A
1 will probably come
2 won't be living
3 probably won't
4 will definitely win

B
1 ~~come definitely~~ definitely come
2 ~~won't certainly~~ certainly won't
3 Correct
4 Correct
5 ~~probably will~~ will probably

### PRONUNCIATION
1 b 2 b 3 a 4 b 5 a 6 b

### VOCABULARY
1 agreement, discussion, improvement, development
2 ability, possibility, reality, weakness
3 happiness, sadness, activity, loneliness
4 relaxation, explanation, reaction, occupation
5 enjoyment, prediction, ambition, creation

## 4.3 Hygge
### GRAMMAR

A
1 How did Bill Gates become rich?
2 Who became President of the US in 2008?
3 Where did the Vikings come from?
4 When do Mexicans celebrate Day of the Dead?
5 Which reggae musician died in 1981?

B
1 ~~What gave you~~ What did you give
2 ~~Who did~~ How did / Did
3 ~~How she~~ How did she / Did she
4 ~~stole the thieves~~ did the thieves steal

### VOCABULARY

A
1 c 2 f 3 d 4 a 5 b 6 e

B
1 d 2 c 3 f 4 a 5 g 6 b 7 e

### PRONUNCIATION
1 night in
2 time out
3 turn off
4 like it
5 make up
6 run away

## 4.4 Reading
### READING

B
1 c 2 a 3 d 4 b

C
1 develop 2 young 3 closer 4 priority 5 research
6 every 7 showed 8 more 9 opposite 10 because
11 guess

## 4.5 Listening; Functional Language
### LISTENING

B
1 e 2 c 3 a 4 d 5 b

C
1 old 2 young 3 cost 4 age 5 adult
6 buildings 7 leave 8 poor 9 crime
10 different 11 change

### FUNCTIONAL LANGUAGE
1 want 2 I'd love to 3 Could 4 sounds great
5 wait a minute 6 Are you 7 free 8 could 9 sorry
10 about 11 it is

## 4.6 Write an invitation

### WRITING

**B**

Notting Hill Carnival, go to see Big Ben, hang out in Regent's Park, go to the theater

**C**

**1** c **2** e **3** f **4** b **5** d **6** a

**D**

3, 1, 2, 4, 6, 5

### WRITING PRACTICE

**B**

**Model answer**

Hi Lucy,

How's life? I hope everything is going well. Do you have any plans for next weekend? I'm going to have a party at my new house. Would you like to come? I'm inviting about fifty people including Chris and Jessica, who you met last time you visited me. There will be music, dancing and plenty of food. I'm going to have a barbecue in the backyard if the weather is good! Obviously, you can stay with me in the spare room. Then maybe the next day, we can go to the beach and for dinner in the evening. I would love to see you again, so I hope you can make it.

Bye for now.

Laura

## 5.1 Work

### GRAMMAR

**A**

**1** Jason wants to be a taxi driver but he can't drive. (c)
**2** Sarah hopes to be a translator because she can speak five languages. (e)
**3** My mom wanted to be a doctor but she couldn't stand the sight of blood. (d)
**4** Tim would love to be a lifeguard but he can't swim. (f)
**5** Sally wanted to be an accountant but she couldn't do math. (h)
**6** Sam wants to become a comedian because he can make everyone laugh. (g)
**7** George wanted to be an artist because he could paint and draw so well. (a)
**8** Zoe knew she could be a pop star because she could sing so beautifully. (b)

**B**

**1** ~~walking~~ walk / go walking **2** Correct
**3** ~~could~~ was able / could ~~to~~ get **4** ~~wasn't~~ weren't
**5** Correct **6** ~~Can~~ Could

**C**

**1** aren't able to **2** Are you able to / Will you be able to
**3** were able to **4** being able to

### VOCABULARY

**A**

**1** ~~skills~~ hours **2** ~~shift~~ wage **3** ~~wage~~ raise **4** ~~raise~~ day
**5** ~~hours~~ skills **6** ~~day~~ car

**B**

**1** take **2** work **3** earn **4** is **5** get **6** get

### PRONUNCIATION

**1** very well
**2** white van
**3** wonderful view
**4** Where's Victoria?
**5** We visited Washington
**6** weird weather

## 5.2 Flip-flop entrepreneurs

### GRAMMAR

**A**

**1** b, must **2** f, must not **3** e, can **4** c, must not
**5** d, can **6** a, must

**B**

**1** have to **2** have to **3** don't have to **4** can **5** can't
**6** have to **7** have to **8** has to

### PRONUNCIATION

**1** can't be **2** must go **3** must not take **4** can do

### VOCABULARY

**1** nice **2** cool **3** fashionable **4** stylish **5** casual **6** cool

## 5.3 Don't call us

### GRAMMAR

**A**

**1** has asked **2** haven't thought **3** since **4** sent
**5** haven't worked **6** for **7** have spent **8** since **9** had
**10** Have, studied, traveled **11** have worked **12** since
**13** have been **14** were

**B**

**1** c **2** a **3** e **4** b **5** f **6** d

### PRONUNCIATION

**1** I've worked here for seven years.
**2** How long has Liz been married to Tony?
**3** She's had that car since she left college.
**4** How long have you known your boss?
**5** They've lived in New York for about ten years.

### VOCABULARY

**A**

**1** in
**2** in / at
**3** for / at
**4** for
**5** in
**6** for / at
**7** in / at

**B**

**1** in **2** for **3** at / by **4** in / at **5** in / at

## 5.4 Reading

### READING

**A**

**1** c **2** a **3** d **4** b **5** e

**B**
**1** L **2** H **3** L **4** L **5** H

**C**
**1** Aisha **2** Joel **3** Xavi, Claudio **4** Margaret
**5** Claudio **6** Joel **7** Xavi **8** Claudio **9** Margaret
**10** Aisha **11** Joel **12** Xavi

# 5.5 Listening; Functional Language

## LISTENING

**B**
2, 4, 5, 6 and 8

**C**
**1** inside **2** with other people **3** Jess decides
**4** get ideas **5** can **6** are dressed appropriately
**7** different from **8** because they want to

**D**
**1** No **2** Her boss was always checking she was busy.
**3** No **4** He had to wear a suit.

## FUNCTIONAL LANGUAGE

**1** f **2** a **3** d **4** g **5** e **6** b **7** c

# 5.6 Write a cover email

## WRITING

**A**
**Suggested answers**
**1** To gain experience and new skills.
**2** The advantages are free training and you can keep any tips. The disadvantages are that it is unpaid and you have to work weekends.

**B**
**1** Dear Ms. Ducas, **2** I would like to apply for the city tour guide internship. **3** I hope to hear from you soon.
**4** Sincerely yours,

**C**
1, 2, 5, 7

**D**
**1** d **2** a **3** b **4** c

## WRITING PRACTICE

**B**
**Model answer**
Dear Ms. Ducas,
I would like to apply for the city tour guide internship. Please find attached a copy of my résumé.
I am a hard-working person who can pick up new skills easily. I have previously worked as a waiter in a restaurant on weekends. The knowledge and skills I developed there will be very helpful because I had to be friendly, polite and organized.
I study English in college and would love the opportunity to practice it further. I also speak some Italian.
Being an intern at your company would be an exciting opportunity. I look forward to your response.
Sincerely yours,
Juan Santiago

# 6.1 Health myths

## GRAMMAR

**A**
**1** have enough doctors
**2** too much sugar
**3** has enough money
**4** too many children
**5** have enough time

**B**
**1 a** big enough
**b** too many
**2 a** too expensive
**b** enough money
**3 a** too small / short
**b** big / tall enough

## VOCABULARY

**A**
**1** a cold
**2** a broken bone
**3** a stomachache
**4** the flu
**5** a temperature
**6** a headache
**7** a sore throat
**8** a toothache
**9** a sunburn
**10** a cough

**B**
**1** b **2** d **3** e **4** a **5** c

## PRONUNCIATION

**1** look **2** burn **3** head **4** cough **5** short

# 6.2 Keep fit

## VOCABULARY

**A**
**1** ~~jogging~~
**2** ~~a marathon~~
**3** ~~biking~~
**4** ~~calories~~

**B**
**1** staying
**2** lose
**3** doing
**4** go
**5** play
**6** joining
**7** burn
**8** work out
**9** play
**10** do
**11** run / do

## PRONUNCIATION

**1** making money
**2** not many mangoes
**3** no more meetings for a month
**4** nine monkeys making a mess

## GRAMMAR

**A**

**1** G **2** PP **3** G **4** A **5** PP **6** A

**B**

**1** writing **2** living **3** waiting **4** working
**5** Running / Playing **6** playing, disappointing
**7** relaxing **8** Watching, exciting

# 6.3 We may never 'meat' again

## GRAMMAR

**A**

**1** He hasn't stopped drinking coffee yet.
**2** He hasn't started taking vitamin C tablets yet.
**3** He hasn't found a personal fitness coach yet.
**4** He has already borrowed Jim's exercise bike.
**5** He hasn't quit smoking yet.
**6** He has already started going to bed at 10:00 pm.

**B**

**1** 's / has just gotten
**2** 've / have already packed
**3** Has, left, yet?
**4** hasn't learned, yet
**5** 've / have just arrived
**6** 've / have already seen

## PRONUNCIATION

**1** sea **2** shell **3** show **4** sake
**5** shocks **6** rush **7** crust **8** my shelf

## VOCABULARY

| W | C | U | C | U | M | B | E | R | N | Z | Z |
|---|---|---|---|---|---|---|---|---|---|---|---|
| J | Q | D | R | L | O | B | S | T | E | R | K |
| J | O | B | H | S | B | T | O | M | A | T | O |
| C | M | M | V | K | N | A | O | A | T | S | O |
| Y | S | H | R | I | M | P | N | H | M | C | A |
| L | R | X | M | C | R | A | B | A | M | A | V |
| L | E | T | T | U | C | E | T | K | N | Q | O |
| U | R | V | I | F | K | P | W | U | Z | A | C |
| L | I | F | E | M | N | V | T | H | P | P | A |
| P | C | X | E | Z | X | U | I | B | E | Z | D |
| L | E | J | E | U | C | H | T | B | W | A | O |
| S | A | N | D | W | I | C | H | S | E | Y | T |

# 6.4 Reading

## READING

**A**

healthy

**B**

**1** reduces stress **2** fall in love **3** brain power
**4** less at risk **5** improve circulation **6** smile more
**7** reduce memory loss **8** good for body clock
**9** It is a myth **10** keep the skeleton strong
**11** lose weight **12** protect you from sunburn

# 6.5 Listening; Functional Language

## LISTENING

**B**

**1** Japan **2** New Zealand **3** Greece

**C**

**1** New Zealand **2** Japan **3** New Zealand **4** Greece
**5** Japan **6** Japan **7** Greece **8** New Zealand **9** Greece
**10** Japan

## FUNCTIONAL LANGUAGE

**1** c **2** b **3** a **4** b **5** b **6** c **7** c

# 6.6 Write a product review

## WRITING

**B**

**1** c **2** d **3** b **4** e **5** a

**C**

**Positive:** highly recommended, definitely worth the money, very happy
**Negative:** poorly made, the atmosphere wasn't great, slightly disappointed, I don't recommend

## WRITING PRACTICE

**B**

**Model answer**

Zumba: Fun fitness ★★★★

My sister highly recommended coming to zumba classes with her and I thought I'd give it a try.

The classes weren't expensive. Only $30 for ten classes, which I think is great value for money. I lost a little weight and feel much more energetic. So they are definitely worth the money.

The biggest positive was that the instructor was really helpful and gave clear instructions. She also played good music which made the class fun and the time went by quickly.

On a negative note, the room it is held in is very small and warm. The air conditioning usually isn't working so it can get too hot.

# Notes

## Notes